Ter[illegible] [illegible]re[illegible]

A d20® System Adventure

Design: Robert J. Toth
Additional Material: Chris Pramas
Development: Chris Pramas and Jennifer Clarke Wilkes
Editing: Jennifer Clarke Wilkes
Art Direction: Nicole Lindroos
Cover Art: Brom
Interior Art: Toren Atkinson, Chris Keefe
Cartography: Hal Mangold, Todd Gamble
Layout and Cover Design: Hal Mangold

Rob Toth's Special Thanks: Chris Pramas, John Burek, Woody Clermont, Chris Flaherty, Pete Jencius, Brian Kirby, Jennifer Kirby, Rob Lawson, Todd Miller, Kim Pratt, Joe Richardson, Winston Sapigao, and Nancy Fitzsimmons (thief/acrobat).

Chris Pramas's Special Thanks: Eric, Dustin and everyone at Wizard's Attic for making this all possible.

Farewell: Sandeep Rao

Contact Green Ronin: greenronin@aol.com
Website: www.greenronin.com

Introduction

Welcome to *Terror in Freeport,* the second in Green Ronin Publishing's series of **d20**® System adventures. This module has been designed for characters who have made their way through the first adventure in the series, *Death in Freeport*, and are ready to delve deeper into the sinister forces controlling the island city. To play *Terror in Freeport*, you'll need the DUNGEONS & DRAGONS® *Player's Handbook*, the *DUNGEON MASTER's Guide*, and the *MONSTER MANUAL.* In addition, *Death in Freeport* contains a complete history of the city and information about the serpent people.

Freeport is designed with minimal detail so that you can use the city in any campaign world you desire. The Serpent's Teeth is a small chain of islands that you can easily drop into a given setting, or you may decide to use this information to flesh out an island city in your existing world. If you've got a good candidate, a simple name switch is all that's necessary. Similarly, most references to gods in this module are generic. When the text refers to the God of Knowledge, for example, substitute an appropriate deity from your campaign.

The Real Story

Throughout the adventure, you'll find sections of shaded, boxed text. This is information for the players, which you can read aloud or paraphrase as you wish. Sidebars entitled "The Real Story" are notes to help you track the complex intrigue. Statistics for creatures and nonplayer characters (NPCs) are detailed in the Appendix, with abbreviated information presented in each encounter.

Encounter Levels

Terror in Freeport is suitable for a party of four 3rd-level characters, though it could be run with more, or with characters of up to 5th level, if you toughen up the opposition. An Encounter Level (EL) rates a given situation's toughness for a typical party of four adventurers.

Although there are plenty of baddies to dispatch in *Terror in Freeport*, there's not a lot of treasure or magic items to dispense. Much of the adventure will be spent interacting with NPCs and doing detective work. Take the nature of the module into account when awarding experience points—story awards and ad hoc XP for innovative solutions are appropriate—so the players know they're not missing anything if their characters don't come away with heaps of booty.

A Brief History of Freeport

Thousands of years ago, serpent people ruled the world. Their empire centered on a continent called Valossa—a vast island of cyclopean cities, its population devoted to the peaceful worship of Yig, the serpent god. Then this great race vanished overnight, their world-spanning civilization destroyed by the hand of the Unspeakable One, a loathsome deity born outside describable space. Most of the serpent people degenerated into savagery—but a few retained their sanity, including some of the cultists who had summoned the grotesque god. These apostates retreated to tunnels beneath the former Valossa, carrying on their uncouth rites beyond the wholesome glimmer of daylight and biding their time until the Unspeakable One could once again be persuaded to favor the world with its fearsome attentions.

Centuries passed. The serpent people and their empire were forgotten. Humans and their cousins rose to dominate the world, including the former Valossa, now reduced to a small chain of islands known as the Serpent's Teeth. Pirates were the first to inhabit the largest of the islands, A'Val, and founded a settlement they dubbed Freeport. It became the buccaneers' base of operations, until their depredations on the high seas drew the attentions of the great naval powers. A cunning captain named Drac realized the city didn't stand a chance, so he struck a deal to scuttle the island's pirates if the other nations recognized Freeport as an independent city-state, with himself as Sea Lord. The result: instant respectability.

Freeport prospered for generations, becoming one of the world's key trading spots. There were rough spots over the years—poor leaders, bad decisions—but the city always landed on its feet…until now.

After one of the rough patches in city history, Anton Drac, a descendant of the city's founder, took the reins of government and got Freeport back on course. But he made enemies. Powerful ones. Walking the docks one night he was struck down by a single yellow-feathered arrow. The assassin was killed, and his body spirited away, before he could be questioned. Thus the stage was set for the man who would bring Freeport to the brink of doom.

Milton Drac, a distant relative of Anton, connived his way into the Sea Lord's chair and bent the Captains' Council (the city's administrative body) to his will. He poured the resources of the island, and the goodwill of his office, into one bizarre goal: building the largest lighthouse in the world, supposedly as a symbol of Freeport's dominance of the seas. The grand inauguration is three months away…and dark forces are beginning to creep out of hiding.

Death in Freeport: A Summary

The adventurers were persuaded by a local cleric, Brother Egil, to undertake a search for a friend of his, a librarian at the temple to the God of Knowledge. The librarian, Lucius, had been motivated by unseen forces to wander the world for five years, searching for arcane knowledge. Upon his return, he began to search for clues to this "missing time"—and promptly vanished.

The investigation led the player characters (PCs) to a boarded-up house: the secret entrance to the temple of the Unspeakable One, hidden in a series of caverns under the city. They rescued Lucius

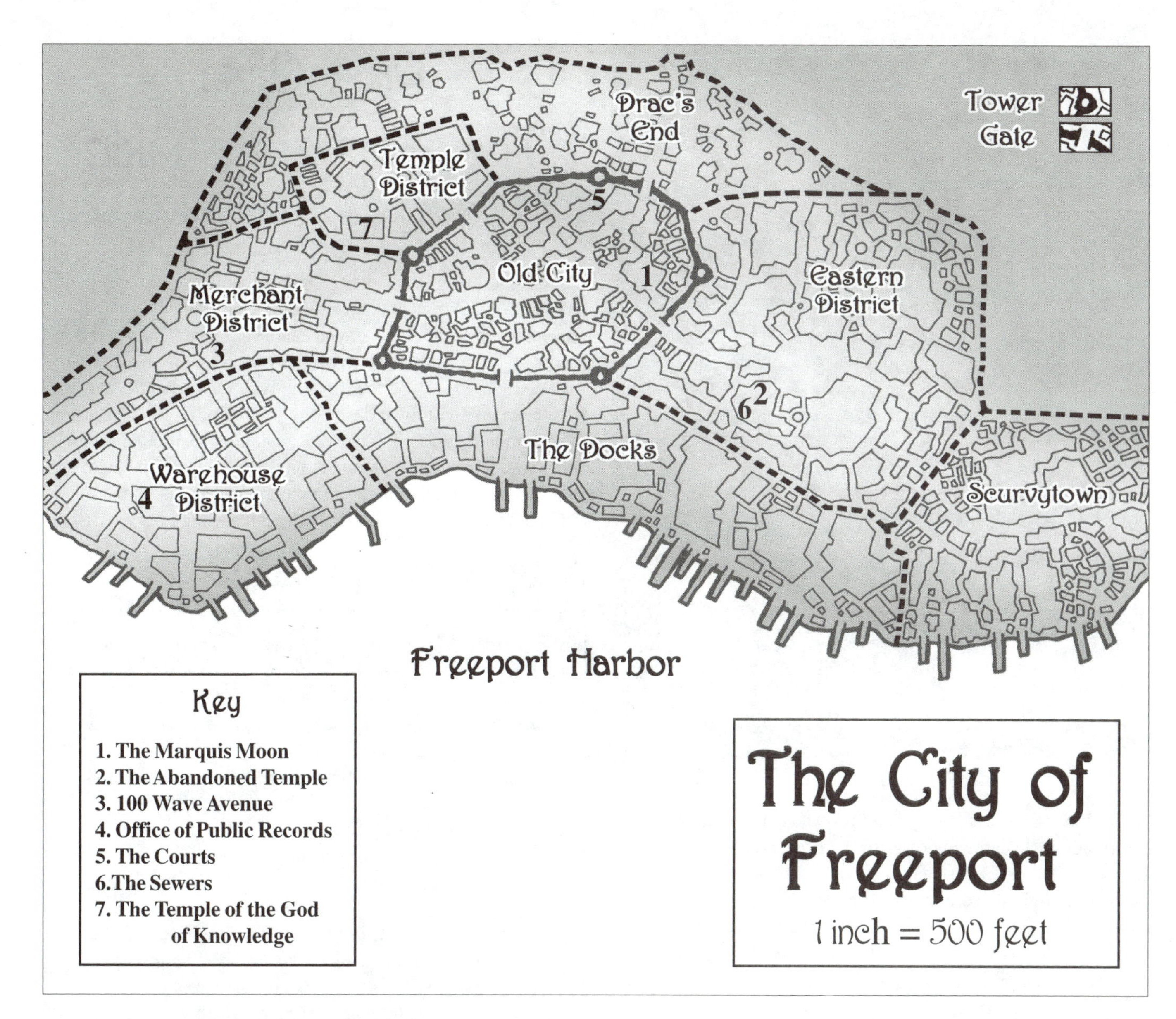

but uncovered a number of disturbing truths. The ophidian cult of the Unspeakable One—also known as the Brotherhood of the Yellow Sign—is very much alive. Its members passed unnoticed in Freeport for years—including Milos, assistant to the high priest of the God of Knowledge and a cleverly disguised serpent man. And the Brotherhood has wicked plans for the port city.

Adventure Synopsis

Terror in Freeport leads the PCs deeper into the intrigue they began to glimpse in *Death in Freeport.* The investigation takes them from the corridors of power to the bowels of the underworld, with terrifying insights into who *really* controls the city. They discover that the Brotherhood of the Yellow Sign has its claws in the town's power elite, but thanks to some clever camouflage by Sea Lord Drac, they may not find out just whom the serpents control until it's too late.

As the adventure begins, the PCs are contacted once more by a very nervous Brother Egil. He tells them that while staying with Lucius one evening, he awoke to find a burglar in the room stealing a scroll. Egil is certain that the Brotherhood have penetrated further into Freeport than anyone imagines. He wants the PCs to investigate Milos's other ties to the city and find out what's being done about the temple of the Unspeakable One.

The PCs search the cultist's lodgings and discover it has been carefully gone over, and several possibly incriminating books are missing. But the burglars overlooked one thing: a tome with a diagram of the Lighthouse of Drac sketched onto the back page, marked with the letter *V*.

Upon leaving Milos's lodgings, the PCs come upon a gang of orcs beating up a hapless messenger. They lend a hand, only to discover they've been tricked—the messenger makes off with Milos's book! A chase through the back streets leads them to the boarded-up building they discovered in *Death in Freeport*.

What they find isn't encouraging. There is a guard posted out front, courtesy of "V"—Verlaine, head of the Captains' Council. Meanwhile, down below, the cultists continue to have the run of the caverns—in fact, they have been shipping their unholy relics to Verlaine's own home!

Part One: The Serpent's Skin

In which the adventurers discover that a snake might easily discard an old covering in order to grow.

The adventure begins about a month after the events described in *Death in Freeport*. If you have sent the characters through other adventures in the meantime, you can have them summoned back to town with a frantic missive from Brother Egil. If you wish to pick up right where you left off, simply discuss what the players have been doing in town during the past month—working at odd jobs, getting familiar with the city, keeping an ear to the ground, and so on. However you arrange things, the action starts with meeting Brother Egil one evening in the dining hall at the Scholar's Quill (the PCs have likely been staying here anyway).

Suspicions Aroused

Brother Egil hails your party with a stiff wave of his hand as he enters the room. Crossing through the tables, he moves quickly and keeps his eyes darting from patron to patron. When a drowsy old sailor drops a plate, the cleric spins and calls out the first syllables of a protection spell. He's embarrassed by his mistake but doesn't seem relieved at all.

"It's good to see you again," Brother Egil says, taking a seat against the wall. "Lucius asks after you. I trust you are all well."

He listens to your stories of the past month and nods absently. Then he takes a deep breath and leans close. "Forgive me for being distracted," he says. "I believe someone is trying to undo the good work you've done for Freeport."

Egil takes a nervous glance around the room before continuing. "Things...have been happening. I'm not sure I can be any more specific than that. Over the past month, I've been sensing a change in the atmosphere. I've lived here all my life, but now the city feels strange to me. The street seems full of eyes but not faces. I notice movement at the limits of my vision. I see shapes at the window when I am alone in a room. I hear footfalls behind me on the street, but when I turn I see nothing. Perhaps it's only nerves. I could almost believe that. But then there was the intruder.

"I was with Lucius when I saw it. Lucius has been...well, it's been difficult for him to readjust. I'm sure you can understand. First the possession, then the kidnapping...we try to make him as comfortable as possible, but there are some things beyond even prayer. For days he has been collapsing at his desk—he becomes feverish and just faints dead away. One of us always takes him home after such a spell. Last night was my turn.

A check of Verlaine's background reveals some troubling information. He came to power from virtual obscurity following Anton's assassination, and he was the one who pushed the lighthouse plan through the Council. Now he oversees that plan, among others, becoming one of the wealthiest men in town—and Milos was one of his special advisers on the project.

In the middle of their investigation, the PCs are approached by a squad of Verlaine's guard. The councilor wants the party out of town—he doesn't like their kind. But at the last moment, Brother Egil bursts in to save the adventurers. His temple has interceded on their behalf, but he also needs them for a special job. The cultists have taken Lucius again, he says, to finish what they started before.

But, like most everything else in Freeport, this isn't what it seems. "Egil" is a cultist in disguise, who leads the PCs into a trap designed to leave them dead and disgraced. Meanwhile, the *real* power behind the Brotherhood of the Yellow Sign is setting in motion a plan to destroy the temple to the God of Knowledge.

Should the PCs escape and thwart the evil plan, they find more shattering revelations, of which the grisliest is Verlaine's murder. The Brotherhood was preparing to lay the blame on the PCs and Egil's order. Verlaine was never part of the Brotherhood—it was his boss all along. As the adventure ends, the PCs are left to figure out what the Brotherhood is planning for the town, and how to stop them.

"I laid him down on his cot and sat to catch my breath. I just closed my eyes for a moment—then all of a sudden I was awake, and it was the middle of the night. I started to stir, but something told me not to. I sat with my eyes half-open, letting them to adjust to the dark.

"I felt its presence before I saw it: a patch of dark gliding across the room like the shadow of a cloud. I was too terrified to breathe. What air I could force down carried a curious odor—something clean but…dense. Something like water on rocks. Cold, mossy caves. Something like a serpent.

"I watched this figure move about the room. Poking through drawers. Examining books. I couldn't imagine what it wanted to steal, since our order takes a vow of poverty. Then it found what it was looking for—a long roll of parchment. It stashed this in the folds of its cape and left as silently as it had come.

"I can't bring myself to tell Lucius. I fear it may destroy what's left of his sanity. I am afraid for myself also, and for the city. I don't believe the Council really is cleaning out the caverns. How could they miss something like that? I suspect something sinister at work here, more than mere carelessness. Milos lived among us too long in a false shape. He convinced my order that he was a dedicated worker—not to mention human. Who knows how many other forms he took, how many other people he deceived? And who knows how many others of his kind are here now?

"We are not a militant order. We don't have the wherewithal to look into this ourselves. But I cannot rest until this matter is settled. I would like to engage your services once again—to find out the real situation at the serpent temple, and to uncover just what kind of inroads Milos made in town."

Egil offers the party 110 gold pieces each, plus expenses, for the job. He also gives them a lead: Through quiet inquiries he has learned that Milos, under an assumed identity, rented rooms at an inn in the Old City. Egil doesn't know the name of the inn, but he knows that Milos's alter ego was Devlin and that he posed as a struggling merchant.

Most likely, the party will want to investigate Milos's rooms and look into the affairs at the erstwhile temple of the Unspeakable One. While they do so, be sure to keep the paranoia level high. For example, make lots of rolls—meaningless ones; ask for Listen and Spot checks—but even if successful, they don't reveal anything. Once in a while, toss in something more tangible, like a glimpse of a robed figure slipping down an alley or tiles sliding off a building just overhead. If the PCs follow up on these apparitions, though, they find nothing. The Brotherhood is keeping indirect tabs on the party's actions, but they are not risking exposure through unnecessary pursuit at this point.

The Real Story

Egil, and the rest of his temple, *are* being watched—but it has nothing to do with the break-in at Lucius's house. It's true that the Brotherhood of the Yellow Sign has taken a keen interest in the clerics, since they brought suspicion down on Milos. However, the burglar in Lucius's home, although it was a serpent person, isn't part of the Brotherhood but one of the last remaining worshipers of Yig. It was searching for a long-lost document that it suspected Lucius had brought back from his travels. This being is masquerading as Thuron, the high priest of Egil's temple. The burglary is only a red herring to get the PCs into the action—but it will become crucial to the story at the very end.

When the PCs return to their rooms, they find their belongings have been gone through. Nothing's missing, but other hands have definitely done some pawing. The innkeeper at the Scholar's Quill (or at whatever inn the party is using as a base of operations) is not part of the conspiracy; she is genuinely horrified at the break-in but doesn't know a thing.

Looking for Devlin

The first thing the PCs need to do is locate the inn with Milos's apartment. Armed with Devlin's name, this shouldn't be too difficult. If the PCs poke around the Old City and ask questions, they should be quickly rewarded. A successful Gather Info or Diplomacy check with a DC 15 reveals that "Devlin" used to rent rooms in the Marquis Moon, a seedy inn of ill repute. Some helpful denizens of the Old City may also add that they haven't seen Devlin in quite a while. This will hardly be news to the PCs.

Location 1: The Marquis Moon

The Marquis Moon is two stories of haphazard brickwork in the Old City. Inside, the mood is subdued. There are better places to eat and sleep in the city, and everybody knows it—from the pair of quietly drunk dwarves in the nearby corner to the scowly guy behind the desk, picking his fingernails with a knife and getting a leisurely kick out of it.

The otherwise unoccupied gent is the innkeeper's son, Ficca (male human Com1). Talking to him for a few minutes reveals that the fingernail trick is his most interesting feature. His father left him in charge for the day, and Ficca repays that generous act by brushing off this group of potential customers. He puts up token resistance if the PCs ask to search the room in question. However, at any show of force—or cash—Ficca slouches away to try impressing the dwarves with his prowess.

The Real Story

Agents of the Brotherhood have been in Milos's room, removing books and other items that connected him to the Lighthouse of Drac. However, the burglars missed one key piece of evidence.

Milton Drac, who has ties to the Brotherhood, put Milos on the project, but the serpent man's day-to-day contact was Chief Councilor Verlaine, who doesn't know about the Brotherhood or the Sea Lord's true purpose.

Milos's Room

Serpent people like things neat, it seems. The quarters are small—a single room perhaps twenty by twenty feet—and you get the strong impression Milos drew a map of it when he moved in to use every inch efficiently. The walls are invisible, hidden behind bookcases heaped with scrolls and shelves arranged with half-melted ritual candles, leaden icons, and a large collection of brightly polished rocks. Staffs, canes, and other ornamental trifles fill every alcove and fit snugly against the masonry. A stove in the center of the room gives off a faint smell of incense.

There is little furniture. No bed, for one thing; the floor near the stove is strewn with thick, tasseled pillows. No desk either, although there is a portable writing-stand pushed against one of the bookcases. Milos's clothes are folded neatly and stacked against one wall.

Everyone in the party should make a Spot check (DC 15) to notice that most surfaces in the room are covered with a thin layer of dust. Milos had plenty stashed away here, some of which is more obvious than the rest. Successful Search checks turn up the following:

Canes and Staffs

DC 10: These are intricately carved, with serpents' heads for handles. There is otherwise nothing special about them.

Pillows

DC 10: Anyone who pokes through Milos's improvised bed finds only several large snake scales.

Shelves

DC 10: One of the leaden figures is a grotesque replica of the idol of the Unspeakable One.

DC 15: Several objects that at first glance looked like large, polished rocks turn out to be oddly-shaped jars containing albino cave rats preserved in a syrupy black fluid. If a character moves a jar or stares into it, the hideous thing inside comes awake, hisses, and begins scratching at the glass

DC 20: One of the jars only looks like it's got a cave rat in it. In fact, the dimly visible form inside is Milos's emergency savings of 20 pp, wrapped in a small cloth bag.

Bookcases

DC 10: The books are interesting but not magical, being scholarly tomes on a number of subjects. A good portion of them deal with architecture, masonry, and other construction-related topics.

DC 12: The dust on the shelves has been disturbed.

DC 15: One book—*An Accounte of Metalls Base and Pure*—has fallen behind the shelves and become wedged against the wall. Sketched onto the back page of the book is a full-page drawing of a lighthouse, covered with arcane mathematical formulas; arrows point to a number of blocks on the structure. In the margins is a recurring doodle: the letter *V* superimposed on a circle (see Handout A).

DC 20: Close examination reveals that, here and there, a book has no dust on it while all the rest have a film of the stuff. Apparently somebody's replaced possibly incriminating titles with harmless ones (*A Monthe Among the Horse-Rats*, *Eminent Mind-Flayers*, *A Paladin in Hell,* and so on).

Stove

DC 10: There's nothing in here but expensive-looking incense, as well as a lot of greasy ashes.

Clothes

Milos's clothes are quite fashionable for a simple cleric but otherwise unremarkable.

A Possible Lead

If the PCs try to question Ficca about who went through Milos's room, they get the same charming response as before. But one of the dwarves, a bull-headed old drunk named Rottenjones (male dwarf Com1), overhears the conversation. As it happens, he saw something odd.

The dwarf staggers over to you and says, "I couldn't help hearin' you askin' after goings-on upstairs. Could be I know a thing or two."

If you take this unsubtle hint to buy him a drink, he readily tells his tale. "I was headin' up to me room one night, maybe a couple o' weeks ago, when I bumps into a couple of strange-lookin' fellers leaving that room. They told me to sod off, saying they was on official Council business."

If asked for any other details, he looks expectantly at the empty mug. Once it's refilled, he says: "I remember somethin' else now. Took me back to me boyhood, it did. They smelled like tunnels of my homeland."

A Shout in the Street (EL 2)

> *As you walk out of the Marquis Moon, you hear a plaintive cry for help! Searching for the source, you see a spindly-looking teenager clutching a messenger's satchel, surrounded by three grinning orcs.*

It isn't likely that a typical adventuring party can resist getting involved. In fact, though, they're being set up. While the PCs are engaged with the orcs, the messenger dodges out of the melee and cowers behind the PCs, apparently in terror for his life.

Creatures

The orcs are just punks off the street, albeit punks with very large weapons. They lose all interest in the messenger when the PCs show up, attacking their news foes with wild abandon.

Orcs: 14 hp each
Cal: 12 hp, Bluff +5.

Tactics: Cal's tactics depend on the obviousness of the book liberated from upstairs. If one of the PCs is simply carrying the book, Cal zones in on that character and tries to filch the book. At an opportune moment, Cal makes a Pick Pocket check with a +2 bonus, owing to his skill at distraction, opposed by that character's Spot check. If successful, he tries to slip away. A character can notice this with a successful Spot check opposed by his Hide check (at a +2 bonus). Should the target of the theft realize what's happened, the "messenger" abandons all pretense and flees down the side streets—to the bricked-up building that once housed the cult.

If the book is not in evidence, Cal takes a different tack. He cowers behind the PCs while they engage the orcs, and then flanks and sneak attacks the most opportune PC. After this cheap shot, Cal flees, leaving the orcs to finish the job. As above, he runs to the bricked up house.

If the PCs go after Cal, he leads them on a merry chase. He has the *run* feat, so he's quite fast. The streets are also bustling with people. Have the PCs make a series of Spot checks, opposed by Cal's Hide skill. He is ducking in and out of the crowd, taking side streets when possible. Try to make the chase fast paced, with lots of frantic dice rolls. You can also have the PCs make Dexterity or Tumbling checks to avoid hazards like carts, rolling barrels, and the like.

The Real Story

The fight is a sham. The "messenger"—actually a cultist, Cal—was assigned to watch the inn and take care of any nosy interlopers. When the PCs went to Milos's room, he stepped out of the inn and rounded up his hired thugs to stage the fight. Cal plans to take advantage of the confusion.

Orcs in the Streets!

Your players may find it funny that orcs are free to roam the streets of Freeport. After all, they are evil, murdering monsters! Well, if being evil and murderous kept you out of Freeport, the city would be a ghost town. Basically, Freeport has always thrived by being an open city. Anyone can enter the city, but while there visitors are expected to behave themselves. Orcish pirates (such as Captain Scarbelly from *Death in Freeport*) in particular have learned that Freeport's resources are invaluable, so it's best to take a break from killing people while in port. As the orc thugs attacking the PCs prove though, not all orcs can show that kind of restraint.

Should the PCs capture Cal, he feigns innocence. He's a simple lad off the street, he maintains, and how could he turn down good money when some strange men told him to ambush anyone who visited those apartments? If the PCs turn Cal over to the watch, he disappears into the system and they never see him again.

Location 2: The Abandoned Temple

Whether the party chases the false messenger or decides to check things out on their own, at some point they'll probably end up at the bricked-up house. If necessary, you can steer them here through Brother Egil's conversation (he is interested in the status of the former cult temple, after all).

You work your way through side streets until you come upon the rotting hovel that once held a terrible secret. It hasn't changed much since you saw it last—a one-story structure of knotted planks with bricks for windows. The only difference is the street scene. Three soldiers are standing guard at the front entrance. From the outside, at least, it seems the building is secure.

The PCs should make a Spot check (DC 15) when they first see the three guards. Each soldier wears an armband with a *V* superimposed on the city seal. If they don't figure it out on their own, have the PCs make Intelligence checks (DC 12) to recognize this as the same symbol doodled in Milos's book.

The soldiers are the private guard of Verlaine, head of the Captain's Council—a figure the PCs will get to know quite well as the adventure progresses. If asked what the *V* means, they answer without hesitation: "It's the mark of Chief Councilor Verlaine. He's overseeing the cleanup of the temple." PCs with the appropriate Knowledge (Local) skill can make a check (DC 10) to recognize the V emblem on their own. Verlaine is well-known by the locals.

Stonewalling

Questions about a person racing into the building are met with hostility: The guards tell the PCs it's none of their business. If the PCs persist, the guards become aggressive. However, with a convincing story, the guards let slip that a worker *did* just go into the building. This requires a successful Bluff check opposed by the guards' Wisdom (none of them have ranks in Sense Motive). There has been a city crew in the temple for several days now, cleaning things up. Sometimes the guards have taken deliveries from this crew—temple relics and so forth—and shipped them out for examination by the authorities. The guards haven't been inside themselves, and that's fine by them.

The PCs can't talk themselves inside without a *really* good story, however—the guards are dumb enough to chatter, but not to leave their posts. An example of a really good story might be: "We're from the city works department; there's a dangerous breakout of cave rats—and if you don't believe me, look at *this*!" Anything that effective reduces the opposed Wisdom check by –5. (An example of a really *bad* approach is shouting, "Look, you idiots, your boss is a snake!" Not only isn't that going to get them anywhere, but it will likely provoke a hostile response.)

If the PCs are stumped, they can try a number of other tactics to get inside. They might distract the guards while other members of the party pry the bricks from a side window (add a +2 synergy bonus to the Bluff check if this is done quietly), or go into an adjacent building and leap from roof to roof (Jump Check, DC 10), then break through the rotten timbers. Waiting for nightfall or a shift change can facilitate such efforts, providing a +2 bonus to any required skill checks for the favorable situation.

Of course, some parties are just going to attack the guards and try to force their way inside. It's not a smart option, though. Even if the PCs have valid suspicions, attacking local deputies with no proof or provocation earns them a swift ticket to lockup if they fail. The guards are pretty tough as well, which the PCs can notice easily enough. Should they manage to muscle past, they'll have to complete their investigation as fugitives—at best.

Creatures

These members of the Verlaine's guard (Byrne, Weymouth, and Franz) are fairly tough, having been professionally trained.

Byrne: 15 hp
Franz: 14 hp
Weymouth: 13 hp

Tactics: If the PCs are foolish enough to engage the soldiers in combat, Byrne (the chief of the group) blows three short blasts several times on a shrill whistle to summon reinforcements. In 5 rounds, three members of the City Watch (human Ftr1, hp 10 [average]), in scale mail and armed with heavy maces, join the fray. Three rounds later, a half dozen more arrive.

Inside the former temple, not much has visibly changed—but there are subtle signs that evil has not entirely abandoned this place. Make secret Wilderness Lore checks (DC 20) for any PCs with Track as they move through the caverns. On a success, the character notices faint footprints and marks on the floor—some of which are clearly not human. There are pinpoint holes in the dust where the toes ought to be, indicating keenly sharp claws, and big, sweeping grooves that could only be made by a tail.

There's nothing to see in most of the rooms here. The cultists have stripped them bare; even curtains and heavy statuary are gone. But you should keep up the feeling of suspense and menace nonetheless. Make secret rolls while the PCs go from room to room. Ask them frequently if they want to do anything *else* while they're here. The party should feel creeped out by the too-quiet temple.

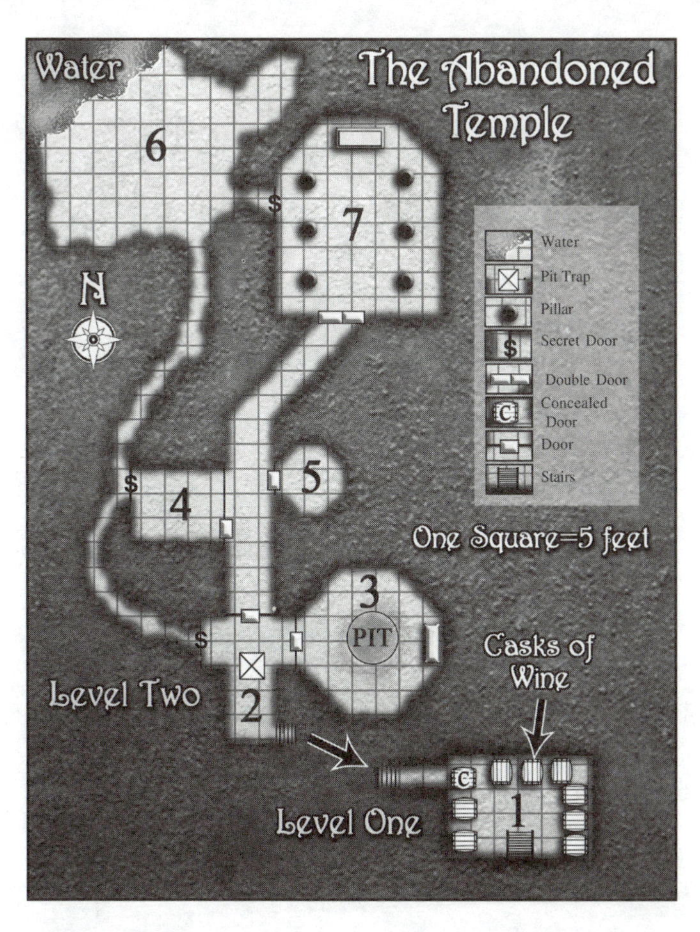

1. Wine Cellar

The cellar is unchanged, except that the cask containing the secret passage is now propped open. Characters who make a successful Spot check (DC 15) notice scratches in the rock floor between the cask and the stairs, as if something huge and heavy has been dragged across the room.

2. Intersection

The pit trap is now jammed open, presumably so as not to hinder the cleanup crews, but there is no one in sight. This ought to raise suspicion—there should be squads of soldiers down here. This isn't how a police force ordinarily cleans up a trouble spot.

The secret door in the west wall, oddly enough, is not open. If the PCs didn't find the door before, they need a successful Search Check (DC 20) to spot it now. Opening it reveals a rough-hewn tunnel stretching off into the darkness…and faint sounds of scrambling and scraping off in the gloom.

4. Treasury

The room is completely bare, but again the secret door is not open. A successful Search check (DC 20) is needed to find this if it was not previously discovered. See area 2 above.

6. Cave of the Degenerates (EL 3)

If the PCs come here before entering the temple proper, they stumble across a small squad of degenerate serpent people acting as bodyguards for a single human cultist, Batora. She is on her way to the surface, delivering a crate for shipment to Verlaine's house. One or both sides could be surprised. Two of the degenerates are carrying the crate, but they drop it as combat begins.

Creatures

You can adjust the opposition based on the number and experience of the PCs, but there should be at least one serpent person per adventurer. Cal (see **A Shout in the Street**, on page 7) can be here to participate in the fight if you wish; he is hiding and attempts to make sneak attacks. Otherwise, assume he has disappeared into the tunnels of the degenerates.

Batora: 15 hp
Degenerate Serpent People: 8, 7, 7, 6 hp

Tactics: The two serpent people carrying the crate drop it upon seeing the PCs, but this delays their combat response (treat as a move-equivalent action). All try to defend Batora until half their number (round down) are dead. At that point, they scatter

The Real Story

Councilor Verlaine has been put in charge of the temple cleanup by Milton Drac. But the Sea Lord has told him to guard only the outside—he's sending a team of specially trained mercenaries, experienced with magic, to take care of the work inside. But there is no such team. It's a cover for the cultists who are still in the former temple. Now that it's been sullied by outsiders, the cave is good only as a hiding place. Devious type that Drac is, he has hidden a new temple in catacombs beneath Verlaine's own home!

The Brotherhood has been bringing sacred objects and other materials to the surface and delivering them, via Verlaine's unwitting guards, to the new base of operations. The guards don't know these "workers," but they have no reason to suspect anything's wrong.

into the tunnels, abandoning the crate and leaving the cultist to fend for herself.

Batora starts with a *cause fear* spell against the most obvious threat, followed up by *bane* and *protection from good.* If things are going badly, she casts *obscuring mist* and tries to escape.

Development: If Batora or Cal gets away, the cultists and their hidden leaders become aware of the PCs' activities that much sooner. This can produce harrying attacks against the party or trouble with the City Watch, who have been told the PCs are troublemakers or even agents of the serpents. The severity of these attacks should be adjusted to match the experience level and the general condition of the party.

Treasure: There crate opens easily and contains some very interesting things. First off, there's an address and other information marked on the outside:

> **From:** Bierce Vintners
> **To:** 100 Wave Ave. (Cellar)

Inside are six golden goblets (worth 50 gp apiece) and a number of bricks. The bricks appear perfectly ordinary, but a successful Spot check (DC 12) reveals a seam running through the middle of each. By chiseling away around the seam and pounding vigorously, it's possible to split a brick in two—to reveal a replica of the temple's strange yellow symbol, printed in shimmering gold ink, in the center of each half.

The players may recall that the sketch in Milos's book had arrows pointing to a number of points in the Lighthouse of Drac. Otherwise, have the party make Intelligence checks (DC 12) to remember that detail. (If Cal didn't successfully steal the book, of course, the PCs can simply check the original.)

7. The Temple of the Unspeakable One

> *The erstwhile seat of the Unspeakable One's cult sits empty—yet somehow it's more ominous for all that. The altar and statue have been hauled off, with gashes in the stone floor marking their exit. The yellow symbol that once graced the far wall has been chiseled away and removed. There's even been some preliminary chipping at the frescoes lining the room.*

If the PCs come here before exploring the cave of the degenerates (area 6 above), Batora and her squad spring through the secret door in an attempt to surprise them. (An *alarm* spell cast on the double doors alerts her to the intruders' presence.) In this case, the group drops the crate in the caverns before attacking.

The Real Story

Milton Drac is in fact a high-ranking cultist of the Unspeakable One and is working with the Brotherhood to construct the lighthouse. In typical fashion, he put Verlaine in charge of day-to-day operations, thus deflecting attention from himself. But he has left his second-in-command in the dark about the lighthouse's *true* purpose—a sinister plot involving the madness of the Unspeakable One. These bricks, crafted by the serpent priests and placed throughout the lighthouse at significant occult points, will help produce an apocalyptic show at the inauguration.

The address on the crate is Verlaine's. The councilor, as well as his guards (who oversee the deliveries), know of the shipments going to his house and that they come from the serpent temple. The crates go straight to his wine cellar, where they are immediately opened by Brotherhood members who sneak in from the catacombs below the house through a secret entrance. The cultists remove the temple relics, leaving only treasure (goblets, coins, and the like), before Verlaine can inspect the crates. Thus the councilor and his accomplices never suspect these contain anything more than booty from the caves, graft in return for a job well done.

Part Two: A Threatening Posture

In which the adventurers learn that a snake in the grass is worth two in the cave.

Most likely, the PCs will want to follow up on the clue they've just found—the address on the crate full of bricks. They may also want to look into Verlaine's background. As they will quickly learn, the two lines of inquiry dovetail nicely.

Location 3: 100 Wave Avenue (EL 6)

> *Wave Avenue turns out to be in the Merchant District. And it's quite a change from the shabby austerity of the Old City. Carefully tended trees and wrought-iron lampposts line the boulevards. Quaint storefronts display expensive foodstuffs and curios; trim, tidy townhouses spill laughter and low whispers through their windows—and more often than not have a private guard stationed out front. Wave looks to be the fanciest street in the neighborhood. The homes have elaborate gardens, some large enough to contain gazebos and fountains. A few of the buildings even have coach houses. And the guards too look more expensive: much more discreet, but much nastier.*

The address on the crate, 100 Wave Avenue, is easy to find. For one thing, it's patrolled by the most guards—four out front, and two more on the roof. All are wearing Verlaine's seal (Spot check, DC 10). Lloyd, captain of Verlaine's house guard, personally patrols with his soldiers.

Just about all the PCs will be able to get out of the guards is that this is Verlaine's house—and they aren't welcome there. Lloyd and his soldiers know about the deliveries from the serpent temple, so they're cagey and defensive about the shipments, but not for the reasons the PCs think.

The PCs aren't going to get past the guards without taking extraordinary measures. They can try to bluff their way in, but Lloyd's been with Verlaine a long time and he's seen a lot of tricks in his day: Even a believable story confers no penalty to his Sense Motive check, and a lame one grants a considerable bonus. As a guideline, adjust the suggested Bluff DCs in the skill description (*Player's Handbook,* Chapter 4) upwards by +5.

The PCs may be clever enough to bring the crate and say they're making a delivery; however, standard operating procedure is to turn over all deliveries to the house guards, who carry them to the noted destination. Attempts to bypass this protocol will be regarded with suspicion. As well, the guards are expecting other members of Verlaine's force to make the delivery and don't buy the standard "Gragnar was sick, so he sent me" line. A successful Disguise check against the guards' Spot (if the PCs somehow obtained guard uniforms) may legitimize their presence here, but getting into the house is still not part of the procedure, and efforts to do so attract Lloyd's attention.

Creatures: If the PCs start making a scene, the soldiers are only too happy to answer with violence. And they've got the law on their side. Fighting a squad of professional soldiers on a private residence, with reinforcements nearby and the City Watch at their command, is a fool's game.

Lloyd, Captain of Verlaine's Guard: 35 hp, Sense Motive +5.
Guards (5): 18, 15, 14, 12, 12 hp.

Development: Should the PCs manage to enter the house, they may be able to scope out a room or two before they are noticed and apprehended (refer to **Location 6: Verlaine's House** for details). If they are caught, go to The Shakedown below; if they manage to escape, they are now fugitives and are being sought by both Verlaine's guard and the City Watch. In this case you can skip The Courts and have the encounter with "Egil," described in **Part Three: The Serpent Strikes**, occur on the street.

The Paper Chase

If they are unsuccessful at Verlaine's house, the PCs will probably want to regroup and find out all they can about the head of the Captains' Council. If they approach Brother Egil with what they have learned, he becomes grave and anxious, urging them to investigate further. He suggests checking the Office of Public Records, confessing that he is somewhat in the dark when it comes to politics—he knows little more than the names of prominent people.

If the PCs ask around town, they find that anybody with an opinion generally holds Verlaine to be a tough, nasty hatchet man for the Sea Lord's operations. Successful Gather Information checks can get below the surface, though, as summarized below.

The Paper Chase

Check DC	Information
15	Verlaine came out of nowhere, just after Anton Drac got killed. It's common knowledge that Anton never cared a bit for him. Maybe Verlaine had nothing to do with the assassination, but on the other hand, just look at how rich he is now!
20	Everybody knows Drac's obsessed with that lighthouse. But some say it's Verlaine who *really* wanted that thing built—he pushed it through the Council when nobody in his right mind would have.
25	Verlaine's got his hooks into everything in Freeport. He bought up all the masonry outfits in town just before Drac announced his plan for the lighthouse.

The Real Story

The Brotherhood is looking for a quicker route from the old serpent temple to the new one under Verlaine's house. As construction on the Lighthouse of Drac heads into the last push, it isn't practical for the cultists to transport aboveground all the occult goods needed for the project. They had already broken into, and explored, most of the sewers on the eastern end of town but were unable to hook up with the western end. From older city maps the Brotherhood's agents were able to determine a disused sewer line, granting an alternative underground connection to the new temple.

Location 4: Office of Public Records

The Office of Public Records is a grandiose title for a disorganized collection of papers stuffed into an old storehouse in the Warehouse District. Pirates don't tend to keep a lot of written records, so these documents largely relate to recent history. It is tended by a craggy, gruff ex-ship's cook named Reed (human Exp2). He spends most of his day searching the files to settle disputes between mariners and shipowners over who owes what to whom.

Reed's attitude is initially unfriendly; he grudgingly supplies requested documents but offers no help. He's been through so many scrapes that he can't be easily threatened, and he's comfortable enough that he can't be easily bought (–5 to Charisma checks to influence his attitude)—but he *can* be charmed. A sympathetic ear for his troubles, a few kind words about the state of his records, and he's yours (+5 to Charisma checks). If the PCs win him over, he can guide them through stacks of records—an all-day job, but well worth the effort. If they get on his bad side, he becomes singularly unhelpful and snaps, *"Who d'ye think you are—Verlaine's thugs?"* If the PCs can establish or restore good relations with Reed, though, they'll find him quite talkative.

Reed strikes up an animated, if a bit grumpy, conversation. "I kin tell you ain't with Verlaine. Good. I've no love for him or his gang. Ye've got no patches—the V*, you know—but that's no guarantee. They come storming in here, out o' uniform sometimes, but I knows 'em just the same. A couple come in only last week, saying they was from the Council and* de-mandin' *maps—as if I's put on this world to serve 'em! Horrible customers! No manners at all I tell you!"*

Reed struggles mightily to remember more details, piecing things together slowly. "They wants street maps fer the Eastern District an' Scurvytown. So I digs up the stuff, and the pair of 'em skulks off to a corner and starts jabbering over the documents. Then one stomps back to me desk and asks for 'more ex-ten-sive *plans.'*

"'Just what would ye be meaning by that?' says I. Sewers, he says. Plans showin' how the sewers in the Eastern District match up with the Merchant District and the rest of town. 'They ain't no such maps,' I tells him. 'Sides, the sewers for the Merchant District is sealed off, with their own outlet, and the manholes need special keys, so no louts can go sneaking underground to rob them rich folk. But they keeps at me, so I brings out what I got: street maps and old buildin' records an' such. That gets 'em excited."

If the PCs ask for more information, Reed hauls out the maps the so-called Council agents were looking at. He grunts disgustedly and points at a grimy spot on an old map of the Eastern District: "Lookit the mess they made!"

The spot is almost exactly where the bricked-up house now stands, though on this older map there what appears to be a sewer grating. Apparently this access was abandoned and later covered up during the house's construction. The PCs can make out a rough fingerprint with a successful Spot check (DC 15), and if they look really closely (Spot check, DC 20), they notice a faint tracing of a pathway through the Eastern District and the Docks neighborhood to the Merchant District.

After examining what records there are on Verlaine, the PCs learn that before he took office in the confused days just after the assassination of Anton Drac, he was a wealthy but unremarkable merchant with stakes in several ships sailing to and from Freeport. He became an immediate presence on the Captains' Council, dominating meetings and managing to bend even the most reluctant councilors to his will. He amassed a power bloc and finally managed to have himself elected head of the council. He then pushed through most of Drac's platform, including a forceful argument for the lighthouse. While in office, he has diversified his holdings, including a big chunk of the city's masonry trade, and has grown considerably more wealthy in the process. He currently oversees a number of projects for the Sea Lord, including construction of the lighthouse—and one of his main consultants on that project was Milos.

The Shakedown

Meanwhile, plans within plans are swirling around the PCs. Sea Lord Drac, having heard about their investigations from the Brotherhood, has told Verlaine that they must be out to embarrass the government and sabotage the planned lighthouse festivities. Verlaine takes the hint and arranges to have the PCs brought in for questioning; he figures if he turns up the heat a little, they will get out of town and stay out.

Almost as soon as the party leaves the records office, a team of Verlaine's guard approach, under the command of Lloyd. The guard captain informs the PCs that their presence is requested at the Courts by Chief Councilor Verlaine, in connection with their unlawful entry into a restricted area—the serpent temple.

The Real Story

Councilor Verlaine

The head of the Captains' Council is a tall, thin, wan-looking figure. He wears a cunning expression about his eyes and is curt with everyone except his friend and boss, Milton Drac. For good reason—Verlaine owes most of what he has to the Sea Lord.

When Milton Drac took power after Anton Drac's assassination, he realized that the Council would be wary of him. So he approached Verlaine, then simply a minor businessman, but one whose cool demeanor and carefully masked ambition appealed to Drac. The Sea Lord made Verlaine an offer: *Serve on the Council and use your position to further my ends. In return, I'll make you the wealthiest man this island has ever seen.*

Verlaine didn't like the idea of being a flunky, but the appeal of filthy lucre was too great. Instead, he kept his pride in another way, making sure no one could doubt his ability and cunning. After a successful election campaign—financed by Drac—Verlaine made a name as a ruthless manipulator on the Council, cultivating powerful allies and weeding out his enemies with blackmail and other unsubtle threats. By the time he became leader of the group, everyone in it owed him something. Drac doesn't mind his underling's ambition. If anything, it deflects attention from his own machinations.

Over time, Verlaine used his position to get a piece of every industry in town. Most recently, when Drac announced his lighthouse scheme, Verlaine invested in the city's masonry businesses—practically a license to mint money. So much money, in fact, that he doesn't realize he is being played for a fool.

Milton's Dupe

Milton Drac is working with the Brotherhood of the Yellow Sign, using his office to carry out their sinister designs. The Brotherhood assassinated Anton and elevated Milton to power so that he could push through the lighthouse project—and the sinister plan behind it. And what a shill he's been. He has nearly driven the city into bankruptcy to pay for the construction, and he installed a member of the Brotherhood—Milos—as a special adviser on the project.

Verlaine doesn't know any of that. Sure, Drac may have killed his cousin Milton, but politicians have done worse. As far as he knows, the lighthouse is just another opportunity for graft, albeit an ostentatious one, and Milos was just an architect willing to work cheap. As for the serpent temple, well—who knows the sort of things people get themselves involved in? But Milos certainly wasn't a snake-man *himself*. Serpent people are just savage brutes, and that nest has been cleared out at any rate. All this talk of an ancient cult is just paranoia from those crazy Knowledge God types.

The councilor believes that Drac's hand-picked troops cleared out the temple and destroyed the relics, while Verlaine's own guards helped haul the loot away. In reality, those "hand-picked troops" were actually members of the Brotherhood. Even worse, they've created another temple of the Unspeakable One in catacombs beneath Verlaine's own home, transferring the unholy ritual objects to the new site.

Verlaine's political maneuvering—and hunger for the public eye—will cost him dearly. As things are set up, all clues point to *him* as the Brotherhood's inside man, not Drac. By tying Verlaine's fortunes to those of the Brotherhood, while leaving him unaware of that fact, Drac created the perfect dupe. Verlaine doesn't know enough to embarrass Drac and wreck his plans—but he has enough at stake in Drac's plans to protect them, even if he isn't aware of exactly what they are. And the Sea Lord won't hesitate to use that to his advantage.

The timing of this arrest is a complete coincidence. But play up the strangeness of it—and the omniscience it seems to imply. ("Just as we were about to penetrate the heart of their operation! Is there nowhere their diabolical claws cannot reach?")

If the PCs decide to fight, it's going to be a challenge. If they insist, conduct the combat until either the PCs are subdued (Verlaine doesn't want them dead, just scared) or the guards are routed. Use the statistics for Lloyd and the guard from 100 Wave Avenue, above. In the first scenario, simply continue with the PCs being led to the Courts—a little bruised and battered, but in one piece. In the second, skip to An Old Friend, described below, but have the encounter occur on the street.

Location 5: The Courts

The guards lead the PCs through the streets to a section of the Old Town near Drac's End.

Lloyd calls a halt when you reach a large plaza. On the opposite end of the square is a wide, low-slung building made of gray stone. The seal of the city is carved above a pair of imposing steel doors. "Come on," Lloyd says. "You'll be waiting here. The Courts."

The guards take the PCs inside and leave them in a large, open area filled with benches. The PCs are disarmed, but their weapons are placed in view, though out of their reach. The guards make it clear they are expected to wait patiently—and peacefully—until Verlaine arrives. If they start any trouble, two dozen constables will be down their throats in a flash.

An Impressive Performance

Verlaine gives the PCs some time to stew before making his entrance. He recognizes them from their work exposing the hidden temple, but he doesn't cut them any slack. He thinks they're working for his political enemies and that they want to link him to the serpent people to cause a scandal. Perhaps they are aiming to have him removed from office or reveal his business holdings and embarrass him. Verlaine is simply trying to protect his business interests and questionable political deals. The easiest way to do this is to intimidate the PCs into leaving town. Adapt the speech below to suit the specific circumstances of your campaign.

To the PCs, this may seem proof that Verlaine is in league with the cultists. The party's research suggests he has helped the Brotherhood gain wide access to the city, including—for whatever reason—the lighthouse project, and now he's lying about it. This is exactly how Drac planned things, of course.

A thin, stern man sweeps in through the double doors. He is wearing rich robes of office on which is embroidered the city seal and the now-familiar emblem of Verlaine. The head of the Captain's Council glares at you a moment before launching into his speech.

"I've seen your type before. A bunch of hooligans, stomping around in search of old junk and loose change. Some big bruiser, a sneaky creep who should be in jail, and someone to patch you up when the goodies aren't unguarded. Usually a little guy in the gang too, just for amusement.

"Don't get me wrong. I don't object to your profession—the world needs you, if only to keep the monsters down. But you people always go too far. You've done good work for Freeport, but that doesn't give you the right to ignore the law. I remind you that breaking and entering is still a crime here. This isn't a dungeon. It's a city, and a damned important one, too.

"I don't know what you were doing down there in the temple. Maybe looking for some loot you left behind the first time. Or maybe meeting friends. I don't know, and it doesn't matter. I don't want you in this city one more day. You'll clear out of here by dawn. There are plenty of boats you can take. I own most of them."

Verlaine's Drift

Verlaine grudgingly allows the PCs to talk, but he's not about to let anything slip (although questions about the deliveries to his house make him visibly nervous for a moment before he regains control). Have a speaker for the PCs make Diplomacy checks to gauge his general reaction. Below are his responses to the most likely questions.

Do you know anything about Drac's intentions?

The Sea Lord has a lot of enemies who whisper behind his back, then run away when he turns around. He's done more for this town that most people appreciate.

Are you working with Drac?

We both have a stake in keeping Freeport the greatest maritime city in the world. And we're the best ones to do that job.

How did you get involved with Milos?

It's no secret the town brought in many consultants for the lighthouse project. Do you really think something of that size sails on one engineer's say-so? Milos was one of those advisers. I can't keep up with the personal life of every single city employee, though of course we're grateful you uncovered the threat.

How are things going with the temple cleanup?

The operation is proceeding. Do you think I'm not concerned about monsters under our feet? I want them gone as much as anyone else.

Did you know there are still serpent people there?

How do people like you keep doing what you do? I'll tell you how—every time a gang plunders a ruin, the place is infested again in no time. Monsters are tough to keep down. We're doing what we can. What more do you want?

Are you sure *any* cleanup work is being done?

How dare you question my authority? Why don't you worry about your next crypt robbery and let me handle the policing of this city.

What about the deliveries to your house from the temple?

Those beasts stole a lot from this city—a good chunk of it from me and my businesses. I'm simply taking back what's mine.

Do you know anything about the bricks being delivered to you?

Bricks? In a wrecked temple? How should I know? Maybe the snakes were doing some construction. Maybe they broke into one of the delivery crates and used it to haul their own garbage.

The city records suggest some suspicious activities. What do you have to say?

If you're trying to dig up dirt, you'll have to try harder than that. Everything I've done is a matter of public record. You're hardly the first to disapprove of city government. More people than I can count have tried to find some stain in my background. They've all gone home disappointed.

Verlaine isn't likely to answer all of these questions, and he certainly won't address more or allow any follow-ups. When he's had enough (that is, on a poor Diplomacy check), he snorts a curt goodbye and leaves. His orders to Lloyd: Show them a bad time, then put them on the first boat out of Freeport. Milton Drac, however, has other plans for the PCs—and his onetime henchman.

Part Three: The Serpent Strikes

In which the adventurers learn that some poisons are not immediately fatal.

At this point, the PCs probably aren't sure what Verlaine intends for them. Lloyd and his guards start advancing, making threatening comments, intending to intimidate the PCs into getting out of town and staying out. To the PCs, though, it appears that the soldiers are toying with them before the kill. Keep the players thinking this as long as you can without a fight breaking out.

Just as things are looking darkest, the doors burst open, and in rushes—Brother Egil! The guards are surprised to see him, but defer to his status as an official of the Knowledge God's temple. Besides, it isn't their job to harass respectable citizens—they're just giving some undesirables the bum's rush. Brother Egil approaches Lloyd and shares some quiet words. The guard captain appears unconvinced, until Egil produces a scroll and hands it to him. Lloyd examines it, grunts, and shrugs. He calls back his guards and allows the PCs to collect their weapons. Egil bows stiffly and comes over to the party.

Saved in the nick of time by their old comrade! Little do the PCs know it's not really Brother Egil but an agent of the Brotherhood, Nikko, leading them into a trap. Nikko is skilled in the art of disguise and has enhanced this talent with a *potion of alter self*; it requires a Spot check opposed by Nikko's Disguise check (at +10). The pseudo-Egil speaks:

> *"Friends, I'm glad I found you in time. I don't know what these brutes intended for you, but I can only assume it was what they have planned for poor Lucius. Yes. The serpent people have taken him again."*

"Egil" leads the PCs out the door, glances both ways down the street, and urges the group down a quiet lane. He looks around nervously, then fills them in on the situation.

Note: Adapt the following as needed to make it sound as believable as possible. For example, if the PCs have reported their findings to Egil in some form, include those discussions here.

> *"It all happened so quickly," Egil says. "I was just down the hall from him when I heard a short, sharp cry. I raced to his chamber to find papers on the floor, the desk upended—chaos. I hurried into the street but saw nothing. I knew you were my only chance, but when I asked at the inn, you hadn't been seen in some time.*
>
> *"I knew the serpents could not have taken you by force, as they took Lucius; it had to be some human agency, even if it was disguised. When I asked a member of the City Watch, he confirmed you had been taken to the Courts. Fortunately, my order still carries considerable weight in this city. High priest Thuron and I found a sympathetic councilor to write up an order making your group wards of our temple, protecting you from arrest and bringing death upon anyone harming you.*
>
> *"So you are safe for now, my friends—from those lackeys, at least. But there is still the matter of Lucius. I fear the serpents intend to complete the job they started a month ago. I don't know where they could have taken him, though. Their temple is empty now and cleared of its blasphemous evil."*

At this point, all the clues are pointing to Verlaine, with the answer likely to be found in his cellar. If the PCs don't remember the business of the sewers immediately, "Egil" drops some choice hints ("I heard about a suspicious-looking group heading toward the Eastern District," for example). In fact, he is luring the PCs into a deadly trap, one designed not only to remove them as a threat but also exact a diabolically ironic revenge.

Development: If the PCs are suspicious and refuse to follow "Egil," he tries to guilt them into a rescue operation by announcing that he'll undertake the mission himself, and help be damned. If this display doesn't melt their hearts, and they check things out at the Knowledge God's temple, they find Lucius alive and well—and Egil missing without explanation. At that point, either the basement of Verlaine's house or the sewers of the Eastern District are the most promising avenues of investigation.

Should the PCs actually penetrate Nikko's disguise, he tries to escape down side streets and give them the slip (heading for the Eastern District, though). He fights if cornered, and he is no slouch in combat. Should the PCs defeat him, they can find a rough map describing the sewers with notes scribbled at key points that seem to indicate a trap of some sort.

The following section assumes the PCs begin their search in the sewers of the Eastern District. If they go directly to Verlaine's house, they'll meet precisely the same resistance they found before. Should they manage to make it inside, skip to Location 5: Verlaine's House below and have them search for the secret door into the catacombs.

If the PCs start poking about the sewers of the Merchant District, remind them of what Reed said: The manholes are locked down, and the key is guarded by the City Watch. Remind them of the number of private guards on the street, and how suspicious a heavily armed party looks prying up a manhole cover.

Location 6: The Sewers

The false Egil accompanies the PCs through the Eastern District, acting nervous the whole way and generally playing the part of fish out of water. When the PCs reach the vicinity of the old sewer grating, he gets particularly upset, asking if they really have to go down there. He puts on a good show, though, of toughing it out to save his friend if that's the only way.

The disused sewer access is somewhat behind the bricked-up house, and the PCs will have to avoid the attention of Verlaine's guards, who still watch the entrance. The grating is buried under scrubby weeds and piles of trash, but some determined digging reveals it easily enough.

The Real Story

The Sea Lord is eminently practical. The lighthouse—and the horrible task it will perform for the Brotherhood—is rapidly approaching completion. He certainly doesn't need adventurers bringing any suspicion on the project now that it's so close to completion. Nor does he need Verlaine to start asking questions—the man's a toady, but the PCs just might arouse his curiosity.

So Drac has concocted a scheme to get rid of the PCs *and* Verlaine in one swoop. He plans to have Verlaine butchered by the Brotherhood, and make it appear the PCs did it. Meanwhile, he has sent an agent to lure the PCs to certain death—while planting evidence that purports to show they were working with the Brotherhood. Just out of spite, he also plans to destroy the Temple to the God of Knowledge, tarring the clerics with the same brush. Losing Verlaine is unfortunate, but the lighthouse will do its work soon enough—and Verlaine wouldn't have survived *that*, anyway.

The Sea Lord, and the Brotherhood, have always had it in for the God of Knowledge clerics and their prying into secret affairs. When Egil indirectly caused the discovery of the serpent temple, that was the last straw. Drac has been waiting for an opportunity ever since to pay back their temple. Now he has one.

His plan is devious and intricate. The PCs are being led into a deathtrap, while Egil is to be branded with the Yellow Sign deep in the new temple to the Unspeakable One. Meanwhile, Brotherhood agents, disguised as Knowledge God clerics, will enter the temple. Using a powerful *sleep* spell, they plan to neutralize the clerics long enough to kill them and brand each with the Yellow Sign. Verlaine is to be eliminated by a cult assassin, who will leave unmistakable proof the adventurers were responsible.

The following day, Drac will make a announcement to the stunned city: The temple to the God of Knowledge *was* the Brotherhood of the Yellow Sign! Councilor Verlaine had suspected as much for a long time, and hired the adventurers to infiltrate its ranks and produce proof. They paid Verlaine back in part, by bringing the serpent temple to light, but betrayed him by keeping the larger secret. They simultaneously betrayed the Brotherhood by revealing its base and then blackmailing the cult. The Brotherhood agreed to pay them off in exchange for getting rid of Verlaine. The adventurers were themselves double-crossed when the Brotherhood refused to pay. The adventurers took to arms; the Brotherhood fell. It all ended with even more bloodshed: The adventurers tried to hide out in a concrete factory owned by Verlaine, but fell victim to their own greed when the crushing machinery was activated. Thus, the city had lost a treasured politician, but it was rid of the serpent menace forever.

A lot to swallow—but, for most of the old salts in town, such a tale of treachery would ring true. The details are sufficiently vague and suggestive. Drac also plans to surreptitiously circulate the "real" story to convince the conspiracy theorists and the free thinkers—Verlaine himself was mixed up with the Brotherhood, and he brought in the adventurers to force a more favorable arrangement. Everybody crossed everybody, and left a lot of bodies to count.

But Drac never counted on the ingenuity and toughness—or sheer luck—of the average party of adventurers.

The sewers are where Freeport dumps everything that's too unsavory for the inhabitants. Think about that for a minute. The stench is overpowering and takes a moment to get accustomed to. Once your eyes stop watering, and you start breathing through your mouth, you see a damp, dripping tunnel with a narrow walkway on either side and a river of effluvia oozing down the middle. The walkways are wide enough for single file. Just mind the rats.

If the PCs memorized, or took, Reed's map, they can easily find their way to the border of the Merchant District. However, the maps are not perfect, and it's easy to take a wrong turn or two—especially with such obvious signs to mark the way. The party is being subtly misdirected to a factory bordering the Warehouse District. Even without the aid of maps, the cultists have left plenty of clues. At important intersections there are dropped articles that Egil identifies, with a shudder, as being Lucius's.

Since the sewers are frequented by Brotherhood members moving secretly around town, make frequent Listen and Spot checks (DC 15 for both) in secret. On a success, the PCs hear scuffling and splashing in adjacent tunnels and spot claw marks on the walkways. This serves only to heighten the tension; the echoing passages make it impossible to track down the sounds accurately.

On the edge of the Merchant District the passage is supposed to be blocked by an iron grating, cemented in place. But a successful Spot check (DC 8) reveals that the bars have been sawed through in the middle. It is a simple matter to remove them and step through. After that, the signs point to a seeming dead end not much farther: a bricked-up tunnel. Another successful Search check (DC 10) allows the character to discern the outline of a door in the passageway tiles.

You think finding the "door to the temple" is a bit too easy? It sure is. The Brotherhood wants to make sure the PCs found this

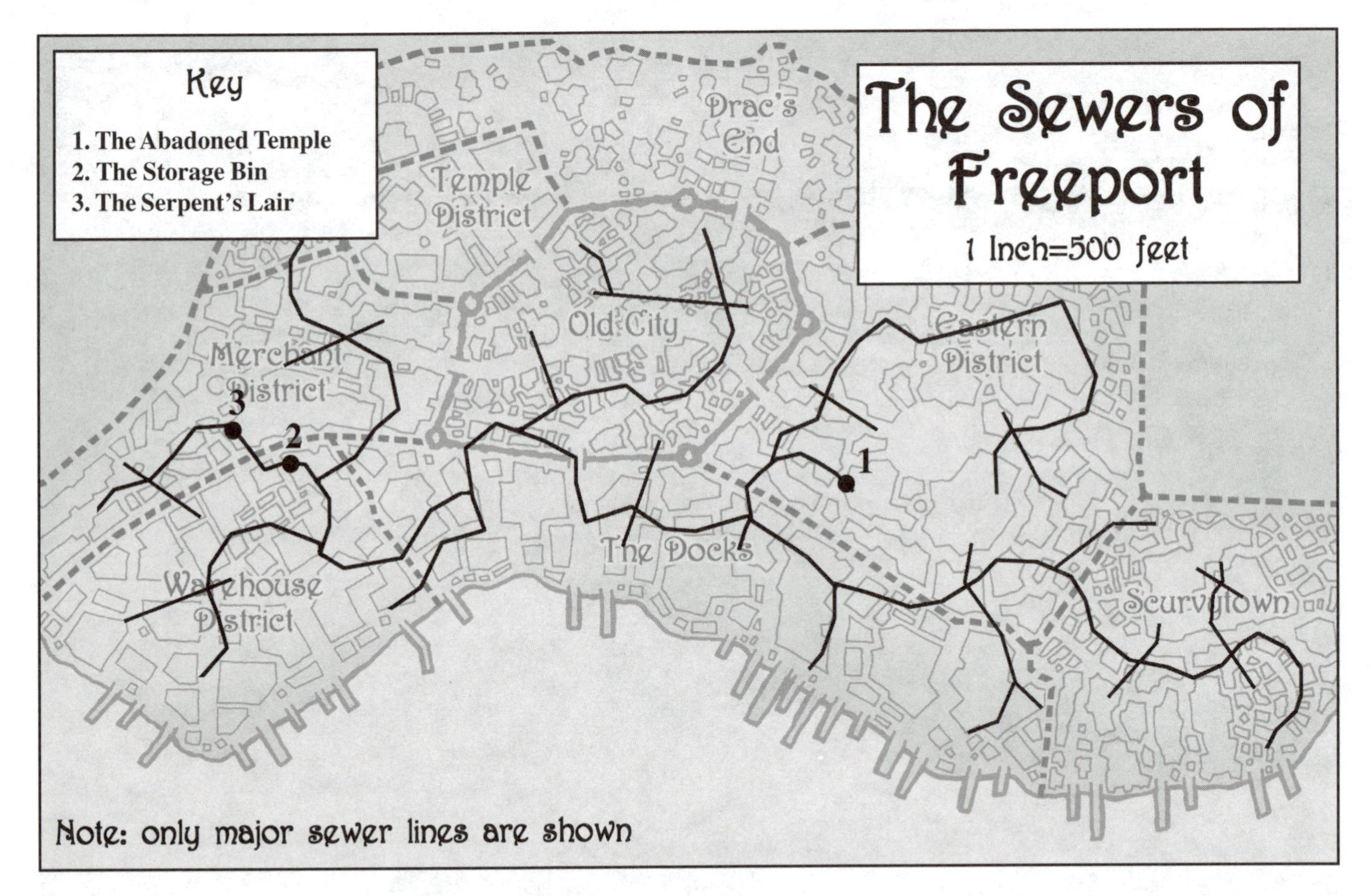

opening. The *real* door to the new temple site is much more artfully concealed (Search DC 25), a little way back up the corridor. Unless the PCs are suspicious, the obvious signs of passage keep them from noticing this. Should they detect the real door, however, or defeat Nikko as he attempts to trap them, skip this section and move to **The Serpent's Nest** on the next page.

Where he cultist has really been guiding the PCs is to a masonry factory on the edge of the Warehouse District, not far from Verlaine's house. With Verlaine's involvement in the city's masonry business, the Brotherhood easily installed an agent to assist in a scheme that will eliminate the meddling adventurers for good. The "secret" door opens into a storage bin, where limestone is dumped before being ground up for cement manufacture. The Brotherhood's fiendish plan: to incorporate the PCs themselves in the masonry of the Lighthouse of Drac!

Rocks and a Hard Place (EL 5)

A latch is found; the door opens easily. And so the trap is sprung.

> *The wall swings open to reveal a thick, dusty darkness. You can just make out what appears to be a small room, barely 10 feet by 10 feet, with a low ceiling. Massive shapes, indistinguishable in the dark, are scattered about.*

Looking more closely reveals that these shapes are heaps of irregular rock chunks. Most are piled up around the edges of the room, though a few boulders are lying loose on the floor. The air is heavy with a chalky-smelling dust.

If the PCs enter this room, "Egil" slams the door behind them, locking the PCs in. There is no keyhole or catch on this side, so Open Lock can't be used.

Should the PCs hesitate, "Egil" attempts to persuade them with anxious comments about the danger poor Lucius is in. If most have entered, he tries to push the last one in; treat this as a bull rush attack.

Door: 2 in. thick; Hard 5; hp 20; AC 5; Break DC 20.

Countdown to Doom

The next few events follow in rapid succession, with a total elapsed time of 5 rounds. This means that the PCs cannot take 10 or take 20 on skill checks—if they're in this jam, they'll have to act quickly to save themselves.

Round 1

Once the door is closed, the confederate in the mill engages the gears that connect the factory's steam-driven wheel to the crushing apparatus. The room begins to shake, and the PCs can hear the roar of machinery starting up. Some rocks slide from the heaps; have each PC make a DC 10 Reflex save to avoid being struck (1d6 damage). If the PCs somehow get above the floor level, no Reflex save is required.

The PCs may be able to notice that the ceiling of the chamber is hinged, with a seam running through the middle. The two halves fold back to allow rock to be dumped in from carts on the ramp outside; the hinges are on the outside. An average lock holds the bin top closed (Open Lock, DC 20)

Round 2

The machinery roar and the shaking intensify. More rocks begin to tumble from the heaps, requiring two Reflex saves per character to avoid damage (1d6 per failed save).

The PCs may be able to see that the wall opposite the secret door is also hinged, opening outward from the top (the rock spills out into the grinding machinery). A successful Strength check (DC 20) can lift it, revealing the crushers a few feet below. On the opposite wall, 10 feet away, there is a small opening through which the operator (human Exp 1) can observe the process; it is wide enough to admit a Small creature.

Round 3

The floor begins to tip and the hinged wall hangs partially open. The rock heaps begin to slide downward and out into the pit, requiring two Reflex saves per character to avoid damage as above. It requires a successful Balance check (DC 10) to avoid sliding out the door and into the crushing mechanism.

Round 4

The floor tips to a 45-degree angle. The hinged wall gapes wide, and the two massive grinding cylinders are easily visible. The noise is unbelievable, as large masses of rock are jostled and ground between them. The remaining rock in the chamber slides rapidly into the machinery, requiring four Reflex saves per character to avoid damage as above. The steeply canted floor is almost impossible to stand on, requiring a successful Balance check (DC 25) to avoid sliding down. A successful Strength check (DC 20) allows a character to wedge into a corner.

Round 5

The bin bounces several times to shake loose any remaining rock (and PCs). Only a successful Strength check (DC 25) can prevent a character from being dumped into the grinding machinery.

Characters who fall into the crusher take an automatic 6d6 damage each round, with no save possible. This is almost certain death unless they can find a way to climb out before succumbing to the damage.

Round 6

The bin returns to its standby position and the hinged wall closes. The grinding racket continues for the next two minutes, however. After that time, the cult confederate (who has been watching through the opening opposite) opens the top bin doors slightly to make sure the job is done.

Development: The PCs can investigate the masonry factory if they so choose. The place is called Crocker's Brick and Mortar, and it's only a few minutes away from Verlaine's house. Crocker, the owner of the place, doesn't know much. He's made a lot of money from the lighthouse scheme but he'll be furious if his machinery has been wrecked. If the PCs describe the operator they saw, Crocker identifies him as Lon, a new employee. "He kept to himself," Crocker says, "and spent a lot of time praying." After the death trap is sprung, Lon never returns to work.

Location 7: The Serpent's Nest

After Nikko locked the PCs into the death trap, he ran down the sewer to the real temple and entered. If the PCs escape, a Track check (DC 15) reveals Nikko's route (DMs may allow a Spot check instead if no one in the party has Track). If the PCs are able to discern the better-hidden door to the new serpent temple and can overcome Nikko's efforts to misdirect them, they can penetrate the hidden caverns and discover a gruesome secret.

1. The Drop

> *The wall swings open to reveal a patch of thick, ink shadows. You can barely see the rough-hewn edges of a rock tunnel sloping precipitously down.*

The tunnel is low (about 5 feet clearance) and permits only single-file movement. It slopes down at a 60-degree angle for some 95 feet. Each PC should make a Climb check (DC 5) to make it down safely. If they use a rope, drop the DC to 0. Falling characters take 2d6 damage (less than normal due to the slope).

2. Corridor

> *The ramp ends in a rock wall ahead and to the left; to the right a corridor, higher than the ramp but just as narrow, extends straight for some 35 feet.*

These corridors were originally tunnels connecting a series of caverns once inhabited by degenerate serpent people. When the Brotherhood moved in, they started to widen the tunnels a bit and smooth out the walls. They haven't had much time to progress, however, nor have they been able to set up such extensive defenses as the old temple had.

3. Long Hallway

> *At the end of the corridor is a sharp left turn. A passageway runs for about 30 feet before turning sharply right, then a long hallway stretches into the darkness—at least 150 feet, with one opening nearby on the left and another farther down on the right.*

A successful Wilderness Lore check (DC 15) reveals clear serpent tracks along the floors, as well as signs that numerous heavy objects have been dragged through.

4. Storeroom

> *This room, a rough ellipse about 20 feet wide, is obviously a storage area. Shelves line the walls, nailed into the rock with long spikes. There are cartons of all shapes and sizes stacked on the wooden planks.*

Among the goods are incense, black candles, oil, inks and dyes of unknown origin, ceremonial daggers, various animal parts

in jars, and the like. All of the old temple's treasure (coins, mundane temple accoutrements, and the like) has been siphoned off by Verlaine, who has been keeping it safe and sound off site. (Tidily enough, Verlaine's holdings will pass to Drac in the event of the councilor's untimely death.)

5. Library

> *This chamber is slightly larger than the storeroom. It, too, is lined with shelves, but these are filled with books—all manner of tomes, written in the incomprehensible script of the serpents. Against the far wall of the room is a desk, whose top is uncluttered.*

The obscure volumes are difficult to understand even with a successful Decipher Script check (DC 30), which leaves a sense of disquiet but nothing of practical use. If the PCs search the desk, they find the drawers full of writing paper and ink. A more careful examination (Search check, DC 15) uncovers a small book bound in leather.

The tome is titled, in Common, *The True and Secrette Historie of the Brotherhoode of Free-Port*, and has the Yellow Sign impressed upon the front cover. The text, also in Common, is filled with illustrations and out-of-date maps. If the PCs peruse this, they come away with a summary of the early history of Valossa, including the appearance of the Unspeakable One (see **A Brief History of Freeport** back on page 3), but with a twist. The final paragraphs are summarized below.

> *The Brotherhood of the Yellow Sign—for that is what the cultists called themselves—persevered and transmitted their black secrets down the generations. The cult found a home in the remains of the once-great Valossa. You know it as Freeport. Over the centuries, the Brotherhood flourished along with the city. And it found a way for its members to move about in the daylight world. Its craftiest, most powerful priests disguised themselves as humans and established a church aboveground: the temple to the God of Knowledge.*

6. The Temple Reconstructed (EL 3)

Moving farther down the hall brings the PCs to a U-shaped stretch of corridor. This section has been enchanted with an *alarm* spell, which notifies the temple priest of intruders. However, the Brotherhood have not been expecting the PCs to find their new temple, trusting in Nikko to dispose of them, so they are not well prepared to deal with this threat.

> *The room at the end of the hall is a good hundred feet high and at least as wide, dripping with stalactites, its walls formed of stone that seems to bend impossibly in upon itself—perhaps a trick of the light, perhaps a result of the abhorrent evil that has been transplanted here. For looming before you, at the other end of this chamber of horrors, is the gargantuan statue of the Unspeakable One! Surrounding this horrific object are*

trappings you recall from the former temple, including the basalt slab of an altar.

You are not alone in this vile place. Among these artifacts of malevolence is a hooded figure slowly waving a censer. A brazier of hot coals, an iron heating in it, stands next to the altar. And strapped to the altar is your friend, Egil!

Creatures

A lone temple attendant is watching over Egil and conducting preliminary sanctification for the planned ceremony. He raises the alarm to summon assistance from degenerate serpent people, who begin arriving from the tunnels in 3 rounds (two per round, until all six have entered the temple).

Nikko may also be present, if the party level is high enough to warrant this, using clerical magic and sneak attacks in defense of the temple. He arrives with the first wave of reinforcements. If he is involved, the EL of this encounter increases to 5.

Temple attendant (male human Adp1): 4 hp, spells: *detect magic, cure minor wounds* (x2), *cause fear.*
Serpent people: 3, 4, 4, 5, 6, 6 hp.

Tactics: The attendant has little combat ability, but being fanatical, defends the altar to the extent possible until reinforcements arrive. He'll try to get away and warn the temple elders if he survives that long, while the serpent people fight to the death. If Nikko is present and sees the battle is going badly, he attempts to slip away and warn the Brotherhood.

The Real Story

Everything in *The True and Secrette Historie of the Brotherhoode of Free-Port* is true—except for the final detail. The document is a plant, which Drac plans to flourish to great effect during his speech after tonight's scheduled bloodbath. "A history found in the very clutches of the serpents themselves," he will announce, "proves that the Knowledge God clerics were actually the Brotherhood all along!"

Development: The interim temple priest (a serpent person named K'Ral) is not present, being engaged in the greater assault on the temple to the God of Knowledge. However, an *alarm* spell cast on the U-shaped corridor has alerted her to the intruders. This forces her to move up the schedule by several hours—if the characters act quickly, they will just barely beat the attackers to the temple.

A Fiendish Plot

If the PCs examine Egil, they find him bruised all over. He doesn't trust them at first, sure that they're disguised cultists carrying out another bizarre scheme. But if they untie him, bind his wounds, cast healing spells, and the like, he soon realizes they are genuine.

The brazier contains a branding iron with the Yellow Sign cast into it. Egil tells the PCs that the serpents were planning to brand him, for some purpose he could not understand. He

doesn't remember much more, though. He was ambushed while on an errand for the temple. What followed were several hours of nightmare—the only thing he remembers clearly is a voice saying, "After tonight, your kind will be out of the way for good."

Searching around the temple, the PCs uncover a hidden niche (Search, DC 12) containing a document entirely in serpent tongue and inscribed with the Yellow Sign. They can make out their own names, interspersed occasionally in Common, but without the assistance of someone fluent in the serpent tongue, they can glean little from this document. A successful Decipher Script check (DC 30) can reveal certain key details—enough to raise their suspicions (see Handout B). This is the outline of Drac's speech to the city, and it's an important piece of evidence. Egil can suggest that someone at the temple might be able to translate it.

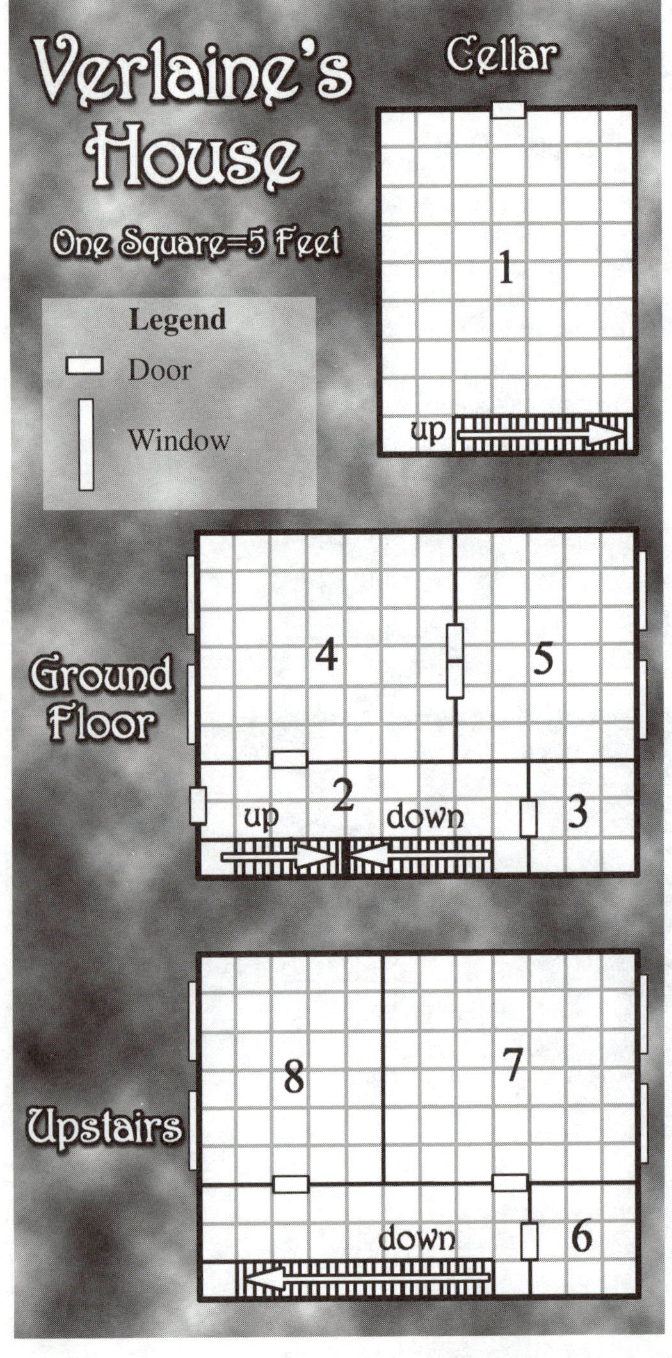

Location 8: Verlaine's House

While they're standing near the altar, the PCs can notice (Spot, DC 15) that the candle flames and incense smoke are flickering in an unseen source of air. A bit of poking around (Search, DC 12) reveals a secret door behind the statue of the Unspeakable One. It is a ramp leading up—a twin of the one that descended into the catacombs. The PCs must again make Climb checks (DC 5, or DC 0 if using a rope) to safely ascend.

At the top is another door, easily opened, which leads into Verlaine's wine cellar.

1. Wine Cellar

> *The door opens onto a large cellar well-stocked with interesting vintages. There is a single staircase going up at the far end of the room.*

There are some open crates lying here, now stripped of their treasure and temple relics. The "Bierce Vintners" stamp is visible on their sides.

2. Main Hall

> *The stairs lead up to a hallway, about 40 feet long. At the near end is a door, which is open; at the far end another door is also ajar. To the left is a staircase going up. As you approach the stairs, you hear a cry of agony from the second floor.*

The near door opens into the kitchen, while the far door exits to the street. None of Verlaine's regular house guard are to be seen.

3. Kitchen

> *The kitchen is small but well-appointed. The larder is full of spices and a variety of smoked meats and fish; the cabinets are filled with numerous finely crafted sets of silverware and china.*

4. Living Room

> *This is a richly furnished room, full of overstuffed couches, chairs, and divans, with large bay windows overlooking the street and a fireplace against the far wall. On the mantle are trophies of indeterminate origin. Over it is a portrait of an elder Verlaine.*

5. Dining Room

A lavish meal is laid out on a long table of polished oakwood. The silver plates and utensils mark Verlaine's station well. Their delicate etchings are artfully rendered, and seem designed to show that Verlaine is not just a rich man, but a man of taste. The sumptuous food spread across the table is untouched and ice cold. It seems the good councilor was too occupied to enjoy his own luxury.

Upstairs

> *The stairs, lined with paintings of Verlaine's merchant freighters, end in a hallway about 40 feet long. There are three doors in the hallway. From under the middle one seeps a pool of red.*

6. Bathroom

Other than a bit of a smell, nothing lies within the bathroom.

7. Bedroom (EL 6)

> *You throw open the door on a bedchamber done up in dark oak and lined with heavy wardrobes, with a canopy bed in the center. Normally, it would be a warm, comfortable hideaway, but now it has been turned into an abattoir. The bed holds what's left of Councilor Verlaine; on the carpet lie four members of his personal guard, including his captain, Lloyd. All have been gruesomely hacked to death, their bodies mutilated almost beyond recognition.*

When the PCs are inside the room, they'll get a nasty surprise—a Brotherhood assassin, Slaan, springs out of a wardrobe behind them! After the first round, he is joined by an accomplice, McNeil, who was rummaging through the study.

Slaan: 21 hp
McNeil: 17 hp

Tactics: With only two of them against an armed party, the assassin can't take the time to make death attacks. He is a respectable combatant nevertheless. The cultists are fanatics, like all Brotherhood members, but they also recognize that the mission—framing the PCs for Verlaine's murder—is of prime importance. The cult can't afford to have their bodies found as evidence, so if it looks like they cannot defeat the PCs, they try to escape with a dramatic leap from the window. These two know the neighborhood intimately and can quickly disappear down side streets, requiring good Wilderness Lore or Spot checks (DC 18) to follow them.

If there is no chance of escape, the cultists smash flasks of alchemist's fire on the PCs and about the room; they stay and burn with the rest of the building if there is no other recourse, thus destroying all trace of their identities.

Once the PCs dispatch the intruders, they find several interesting items on their persons. Both are carrying numerous valuables—golden goblets, silverware, jewelry, and coins, about 3,000 gp total. If the PCs decide to take the swag, remind them that this is no dungeon—they're fleeing a crime scene with stolen goods. (If they take it anyway, there could be serious repercussions later, or at least a lot of explaining to do.)

McNeil possesses a rough map of the temple to the God of Knowledge—with arrows pointing to the two main entrances to the building. Slaan also has a document, written in Common, allegedly addressed to the PCs by Verlaine:

As a duly elected officer of the City of Freeport, I appoint [Insert the names of the PCs' here] *deputies of this Council, empowered to carry out, with full discretion and authority, the infiltration of the temple to the God of Knowledge and uncover what secrets it may hold.*

Signed,

Councilor Verlaine

Development: If the cultists make their escape, they warn K'Ral of the party's interference and may be present at the attack (see **Part Four: The Siege**, detailed on page 24). The incriminating note can't be left in Verlaine's house now, so they try to plant it in the PCs' room at the inn.

The Real Story

The cultists were going to plant the phony deputation order in Verlaine's study—"proof" of Drac's version of the massacre. The map was distributed to a number of Brotherhood agents, who are to descend upon the temple tonight and carry out the remainder of their grisly scheme. They were planning to stash the loot in the PCs' lodgings, to show just what kind of low-down double-crossers they were. (Of course, the PCs may aid in their own framing if they carry off the loot.)

Slaan's document isn't likely to make much sense, but the map should make something click. If the players still aren't getting it, have the PCs make Intelligence checks (DC 10) to remember what Egil heard about the Brotherhood wiping his order out tonight. This ought to be enough to make them realize that the Brotherhood plan to attack the temple—tonight! There's not a moment to lose!

8. Study

This room yields a mess. It is lined with bookcases whose contents have been spilled onto the floor; a big, dark-wood desk has gotten similar treatment. The cultists destroyed most of the papers in the room (nothing incriminating, they just wanted to make it look convincing). They were going to place the PCs' "contract" near the top of the heap.

Part Four: The Siege

The PCs, with Egil in tow, can slip out of Verlaine's place fairly easily. They can use the secret passage again or try the street—the other guards on the block aren't paid to watch any buildings but their own, and they don't pay the adventurers much mind.

If the PCs try to contact a member of the Watch on the way back to the temple of the God of Knowledge, they find that, mysteriously, none are to be found. Drac has pulled them back to the Courts and the Council building on a pretence of heightened security, so as to facilitate the temple invasion.

Location 9: The Temple

When they arrive, the PCs can gain an audience with the high priest, Thuron, if they insist on the importance of their message. The high priest is initially distrustful of the PCs, but he believes Egil's story. If the PCs have brought the recovered documents with them, he reacts with alarm.

The old cleric folds the documents carefully and returns them to you. His voice is subdued but troubled. "I've known this day had to come, since I first learned of the activities of the Brotherhood in Freeport. There was no way any human agency could destroy them. They would return to seek vengeance on those who would hinder their diabolical schemes. These documents prove it.

"Should we survive this night, I will tell you what is contained herein. But there is no time now. They will be upon us—soon, and in force. We must secure the temple. Egil, wake the clergy and have them begin spells of protection."

To you, the old cleric says, "I will not abandon this holy place to the Brotherhood's loathsome depredations. And I will not have the order hunted down and murdered one by one. We will make our stand, and we will trust in our god to protect us.

"My friends, I would ask you to stay and help. I will give you all the rewards this simple order can spare. We may have the god on our side—but steel never hurt, either, as you well know."

If the PCs agree to help, Thuron suggests they wait at the entrances marked on the map. He figures that the Brotherhood planned to catch the clerics asleep and unprepared. With any luck, they won't realize their scheme has been found out and will simply attack as planned.

Egil and Thuron move off to rouse the clerics. The PCs just about make it to the marked entrances as the doors start to open.

The Brotherhood Attacks (EL 6)

The PCs are confronted by five Knowledge God clerics at each entrance, many of whom are sporting wicked wounds. These persons claim that they were out picking up groceries and dry goods for the temple (which they can produce on demand). While passing through a darkened street in the Old City, they were ambushed by shadowy figures in robes, carrying long, crooked knives. Everything happened too quickly for them to see anything. They got away but are sure they were being followed, so they split up to try to throw off their pursuers. If the PCs call on Thuron or Egil, they identify the clerics as legitimate.

Uncovering the Ruse

Most of the false clerics attempt to confuse the situation by shouting out conflicting suggestions: evacuate, call the Watch, leave the temple to take care of its own, and so on. K'Ral acts reasonable, although scared, not obviously villainous. She even suggests using *detect magic* or *discern lies* as a good way to test for intruders. She's wearing a *ring of mind shield,* which conceals her true intention from prying spellcasters, and hopes to salvage the operation at the cost of the rest of the strike squad.

A really good Spot check (DC 20) lets a character notice the heavy gold ring on K'Ral's finger. If that doesn't raise suspicion, have the character make an Intelligence check (DC 15) to remember something Egil said long ago: His order takes a vow of poverty.

Failing that, try another Spot Check (DC 20) to notice a faint scent of caves on one of the "clerics." On a success, subsequent checks (DC 15) can detect the odor around other clerics as well. Only about half of them have a detectable smell, though; some are infiltrators in city institutions who have been living above ground.

If questioned about their backgrounds, or about the Knowledge God's temple, the disguised cultists become evasive. They can give plausible enough answers to general questions on temple operations, and even the layout of their rooms (Milos did *very* complete surveys). But they start to fall down on personal questions—lies that can be detected by magic.

In the unlikely event the PCs don't reveal *any* of the imposters, Thuron can step in to lend a hand, explaining that he has a "special skill" in this area.

Creatures

Once revealed, or if Thuron takes action to identify the intruders, K'Ral gives the attack order.

K'Ral: 25 hp
Cultists: 5, 6, 7, 7, 8 hp (east entrance); 4, 6, 6, 6, 7 hp (west entrance)

Tactics: If they're identified, half of the disguised cultists rush Thuron, the rest for Egil. To confuse the situation, K'Ral pretends to defend the temple (holding back her blows; the blood disguises this fact) until she can get a clear shot at the party's most obvious threat, such as a tough fighter or a wizard. She attacks individual PCs in descending order of perceived danger and tries for flanking bonuses whenever possible, taking advantage of the general confusion to avoid being noticed as the attacker. She'll attempt an opportunistic attack on Thuron if at all possible (although the aged cleric is tougher than he looks).

Unless K'Ral is revealed by the time the fight is over, she is still in a position to cause great damage to the temple. Looking around after the fight, the PCs may realize (Spot, DC 15) that their erstwhile ally is nowhere to be seen. A search of the temple finds a couple of the cells locked. In one of these, K'Ral has already dispatched a pair of minor temple attendants, and she is in the process of putting the sword to two more in the other. If interrupted, she fights to the death in an effort to do as much damage as possible.

Development: In the unlikely event that Thuron is killed in the battle, the PCs are in for a nasty surprise: The old priest's body reverts to the horrid form of a serpent man! Egil knows nothing of this and reacts with shock. In this situation, you'll have to convert much of the conversation below into documents hidden in the high priest's quarters.

Options: You may find that running a simultaneous combat at two different locations is confusing. A good way to handle this is to simply have one big initiative order and treat the whole affair as a single combat. You may find that using miniatures helps you remember who is at which location. If all this sounds like too much of a hassle, you can make the Brotherhood attack come from only one direction, and pile everyone into one location for the final showdown. PCs may thus waste precious time guarding a safe location, and they'll have to hustle to help their friends fight off the real attack.

The Real Story

Both groups are fakes, composed of human cultists disguised with *alter self* potions and artfully smeared with blood from the local slaughterhouse. (A Spot check to see through the disguise is opposed by Disguise checks at a +10 bonus.) The Brotherhood murdered the unfortunate clerics and appropriated their garb.

The group at the western door is led by K'Ral, a serpent cleric in human form. K'Ral didn't expect to find the PCs here; the plan was to be let in, then wreak havoc after the clerics went to bed. She quickly concocted the attack story in an attempt to take control of the new situation. The rest of the cultists are clever enough to follow her lead and act realistically.

If Slaan or McNeil made their escape from Verlaine's house, Slaan is with the unaccompanied clerics and McNeil is with K'Ral's group.

Aftermath: Thuron's Confession

After the battle, Thuron, Egil, and the other surviving clerics work healing magic on the adventurers. Once he is sure the temple is secure, Thuron leads the PCs and Brother Egil to the temple tombs.

The tombs are cold, dark, and deathly still, but the feeling is reverent rather than grim. A luminescent moss hangs from the marble wall, giving off a hint of sandalwood and a gentle yellow glow. Thuron runs his hands along the moss and chuckles softly to himself. Then he lowers his eyes.

"Here I must make a confession. I have lied to you all. I went astray for the best of reasons—but nonetheless I went astray. I can only swear to you I had no part in what you are about to see."

With that, Thuron speaks a few hushed syllables in prayed and slides open a crypt. There is a rush of air, a billow of incense, and you find yourself looking at the body of—Thuron! He seems eminently peaceful in death.

"I am not Thuron, as you can see. My name is K'Stallo. I am the last priest of Yig.

Adventure Seeds

No one expects you to put your campaign on hold while you wait for *Madness in Freeport*. Here are some adventure ideas to keep your party busy while we prepare the climax of the Freeport trilogy. Also don't forget to check out *Focus on Freeport*, a monthly feature on the Green Ronin website that provides new material to flesh out the city. Check out **www.greenronin.com** for more information.

A New Ally

K'Stallo's fate is left vague at the end of the adventure. He may simply leave the city, and put it on the PCs to explain the death of Thuron. Alternately, he may conspire with the PCs to keep up his charade. If K'Stallo continues his impersonation, he can find out all sorts of interesting information. He could easily unearth items of interest and then send the PCs on missions throughout the city or beyond. A typical adventure might be the location and exploration of serpent people ruins on an obscure island.

A Finger a Week

The PCs run into Brother Egil one day and notice that he's been roughed up. He brushes of the incident, blaming it on local toughs. A few days later they see him again, and his left hand is bandaged. It seems that the good brother is missing his pinky finger. A little prodding and Egil shares his shameful secret. As the PCs may recall, Egil's order takes a vow of poverty. And yet Egil had a large amount of gold to hire the PCs on two different occasions. As it turns out, he borrowed the gold from a moneylender and now it's time to pay the man back. Brother Egil hasn't been able to raise the money, so the moneylender's thugs have taken his pinky, and promised to take another finger for each week the cleric doesn't pay. The PCs may take it up on themselves to get involved, thus encountering the criminal underworld of Freeport for the first time. They may take on the moneylender, but he has powerful friends…

On the High Seas

The PCs find out that exotic goods are flowing into Freeport for the construction of the lighthouse. They may then decide to get a ship of their own and engage in a little enlightened piracy (which is, after all, a Freeport tradition). Locating and interdicting ships with vital supplies may slow the construction of the temple while the PCs try to figure out what Drac's plot is all about. Swashbuckling fights on the high seas are always good fun.

"The Brotherhood were not the only serpent people to survive the destruction of Valossa with their intellects intact. Yig preserved some of his faithful in the farthest corners of the world. But evil—and stupidity—have a greater attraction over the centuries than does peaceful worship. Many of my number reverted to simple animals, or worse yet, joined the Brotherhood.

"Lucius found us, during his wanderings, in a small mountain village far to the north. I realized the knowledge he had accumulated might be able to lead us to a closer communion with Yig—an understanding of the divine that has all but faded away over the centuries. So I followed him during his search. I followed him home.

"I slipped into this temple in human guise one evening to look through the scrolls Lucius had brought back from his wanderings. While I was searching, I discovered Thuron dead at his desk. His heart had given out during the night. At that moment I made a fateful choice. Perhaps not a wise one, or even a brave one, but one that made the most sense. I took Thuron's place and devoted myself to the study of the scrolls. I even slipped into Lucius's chambers one evening to see if he had held onto any others. I believe I startled you, Egil. For that I apologize.

"I should have spotted Milos at once, but I was too engrossed in my work. When I learned of your adventures with the Brotherhood, I should have abandoned my charade. But I was too greedy for knowledge.

"Now I will render you the only service I can—far too little, far too late. I will translate these documents. The one bearing your names and Verlaine's purports to be a contract between you and the Brotherhood of the Yellow Sign. Obviously, you and I were to be branded with the same instrument as poor Egil, to defame us.

"The other document promises much greater danger for Freeport—and for the world. It is a public speech, an explanation tonight's events. I will read it without remarking upon the obvious—it is all lies."

Refer to Handout B for the complete text of this document.

K'Stallo looks up, concern etched in his face. "It is the next part of the document that troubles me the most. For the note is addressed to Sea Lord Drac. And his name is marked with the Yellow Sign."

What will Drac do now that his scheme has been foiled? What was Milos putting in those lighthouse plans? And will the Unspeakable One play a return engagement in Freeport?

Madness in Freeport, the conclusion of the trilogy, will answer all those questions, and more. Watch the Green Ronin Web site for a release date.

Until then, watch for snakes!

Appendix 1: Statistics

Townsfolk and Friendly Characters

Brother Egil

male human Clr2: hp 15; AC 11 (+1 Dex); Atk +1 melee (1d6, club/improvised weapon); SQ spells; AL NG; SV Fort +4, Ref +1, Will +5.

Skills and Feats: Concentration +2, Decipher Script +1, Heal +2; Enlarge Spell, Maximize Spell.

Spells Prepared (4/4): 0—*detect magic, guidance* (x2), *light*; 1st—*bless, protection from evil**, sanctuary, shield of faith.*

*Domain Spell. Domains: Good (+1 to cast good spells); Knowledge (+1 to cast divinations).

Clergy of the God of Knowledge

human Adp1 (20): hp 5 (average); AC 11 (+1 Dex); Atk +0 melee (1d6, club/improvised weapon); SQ spells; AL NG; SV Fort +1, Ref +1, Will +4.

Skills and Feats: Concentration +5, Decipher Script +3, Heal +6; Enlarge Spell, Improved Initiative.

Spells Prepared (3/2): 0—*cure minor wounds, detect magic, light*; 1st—*bless, protection from evil.*

Thuron, a.k.a. K'Stallo

male serpent person Clr4: hp 23; AC 11 (+1 natural); Atk +4 melee (1d6+1, club/improvised weapon); SQ darkvision 60 ft., polymorph self, spells; AL CG; SV Fort +4, Ref +1, Will +7; Str 12, Dex 11, Con 10, Int 14, Wis 16, Cha 13.

Skills and Feats: Concentration +6, Hide +2, Knowledge (arcana) +9, Knowledge (religion) +9, Move Silently +2; Alertness, Combat Casting, Improved Initiative, Still Spell.

Spells Prepared (5/5/4): 0—*detect magic, light, purify food and drink, read magic, resistance*; 1st—*bless, comprehend languages, protection from evil*, remove fear, sanctuary*; 2nd—*aid*, hold person, remove paralysis, spiritual weapon.*

*Domain Spell. Domains: Good (+1 to cast good spells); Knowledge (+1 to cast divinations).

Creatures and Unnamed Opponents

Degenerate Serpent People

CR 1/2; Medium-size monstrous humanoid (6 ft. tall, average); HD 1d8+1; hp 5 (average); Init +4 (Improved Initiative); Spd 30 ft., swim 15 ft.; AC 13 (+1 natural, +2 large shield); Atk +2 melee (1d8+1/crit 20/x3, shortspear) or +2 melee (1d4+1, bite and poison), +1 ranged (1d6+1, javelin); AL CE; SV Fort +1, Ref +2, Will +0; Str 13, Dex 11, Con 13, Int 6, Wis 7, Cha 8.

Skills and Feats: Climb +5, Escape Artist +4, Hide +4; Improved Initiative.

Orcs

War2: CR 1; Medium-size humanoid (6-ft. tall); HD 2d8+2; hp 14 ; Init +1; Spd 30 ft.; AC 14 (+2 Dex, +2 leather); Atk +3 melee (1d8+3/x2, battle axe or short spear); SV Fort +4, Ref +2, Will –1; AL N; Str 16, Dex 14, Con 12, Int 10, Wis 9, Cha 8.

Skills and Feats: Intimidate +4, Spot +2; Dodge

Possessions: 15 gp

Verlaine's Guard

human War2: CR 1; Medium-size humanoid (6-ft. 2-in. tall, average); HD 2d8+4; hp 15 (average); Init +5 (+1 Dex, +4 Improved Initiative); Spd 20 ft.; AC 15 (+1 Dex, +4 scale); Atk +3 melee (1d10+1/crit 19–20/x2, bastard sword); SV Fort +4, Ref +1, Will –1; AL N; Str 13, Dex 12, Con 14, Int 9, Wis 9, Cha 8.

Skills and Feats: Climb +1, Listen +2, Intimidate +4; Improved Initiative, Exotic Weapon Proficiency (bastard sword).

Named Opponents

Batora

female human Clr2: CR 2; Medium-size humanoid (5 ft. 10 in. tall); HD 2d8+3; hp 15; Init +1 (Dex); Spd 20 ft.; AC 16 (+1 Dex, +5 chainmail); Atk +2 (1d6+1/x3, halfspear); AL CE; SV Fort +3, Ref +1, Will +5; Str 12, Dex 13, Con 11, Int 11, Wis 14, Cha 10.

Skills and Feats: Concentration +5, Hide +3, Knowledge (arcana) +5, Listen +3, Move Silently +3; Combat Casting, Toughness.

Spells Prepared (4/4): 0–*detect magic, read magic, resistance* (x2); 1st–*bane, cause fear, obscuring mist, protection from good*.*

*Domain Spell. Domains: Destruction (smite 1/day, +4 attack, +2 damage); Evil (+1 to cast evil spells).

Byrne

male human Ftr2: CR 2; Medium-size humanoid (6-ft. 4-in. tall); HD 2d10+2; hp 15; Init +6 (+2 Dex, +4 Improved Initiative); Spd 20 ft.; AC 16 (+2 Dex, +4 scale); Atk +2 melee (1d10+2/crit 19—20/x2, bastard sword); SV Fort +4, Ref +2, Will +0; AL N; Str 14; Dex 15; Con 12; Int 11; Wis 10; Cha 9.

Skills and Feats: Intimidate +4, Listen +2, Spot +3; Dodge, Exotic Weapon Proficiency (bastard sword), Improved Initiative, Power Attack.

Possessions: 23 gp.

Cal

male human Rog2: CR 2; Medium-size humanoid (5-ft. 6-in. tall); HD 2d6+2; hp 12; Init +3; Spd 30 ft.; AC 13 (+3 Dex); Atk +4 melee (1d4, dagger); SA sneak attack +1d6; SQ evasion; AL NE; SV Fort +1, Ref +6, Will +1; Str 11, Dex 16, Con 12, Int 14, Wis 13, Cha 10.

Skills and Feats: Bluff +5, Disguise +5, Escape Artist +8, Gather

Information +5, Hide +8, Listen +6, Move Silently +8, Open Lock +6, Pick Pocket +8, Search +7, Spot +6, Tumble +5; Run, Weapon Finesse.

Franz

human War2: CR 1; Medium-size humanoid (6-ft. tall); HD 2d8+2; hp 14 ; Init +5 (+1 Dex, +4 Improved Initiative); Spd 20 ft.; AC 15 (+1 Dex, +4 scale); Atk +3 melee (1d10+1/crit 19–20/x2, bastard sword); SV Fort +4, Ref +1, Will –1; AL N; Str 13, Dex 13, Con 12, Int 10, Wis 9, Cha 12.

Skills and Feats: Intimidate +4, Listen +2, Spot +2; Exotic Weapon Proficiency (bastard sword), Improved Initiative.

Possessions: 15 gp.

K'Ral

female serpent person Ftr2/Sor1/Clr1: CR 4; Medium-size monstrous humanoid (5-ft. 9-in. tall); HD 2d10 (fighter) + 1d4 (sorcerer) + 1d8 (cleric); hp 25; Init +5 (+1 Dex, +4 Improved Initiative); Spd 20 ft., swim 5 ft.; AC 17 (+1 Dex, +1 natural, +5 chainmail);-Atk +4 melee (2d4+1/18–20/x32, falchion), +3 ranged (1d6/x3, shortbow); SA spells; SQ darkvision 60 ft., polymorph self 3/day; AL CE; SV Fort +5, Ref +1, Will +4; Str 12, Dex 13, Con 11, Int 12, Wis 13, Cha 11.

Skills and Feats:3 Concentration +5, Hide +3, Intimidate +3, Knowledge (arcana) +5, Move Silently +2; Alertness, Combat Casting, Improved Initiative, Point Blank Shot, Weapon Focus (falchion).

Possessions: Ring of mind shield, 20 pp.

Spells: Known (5/3): 0—daze (x2), *detect magic, ray of frost; 1st—magic weapon, shield. Prepared (3/3): 0—detect magic, resistance* (x2); 1st—*bane, cause fear*, doom.*

*Domain Spell. Domains: Destruction (smite 1/day, +4 attack, +2 damage); Evil (+1 to cast evil spells).

Lloyd

male human Ftr4: CR 4; Medium-size humanoid (6-ft. 5-in. tall); HD 4d10+8; hp 35; Init +5 (+1 Dex, +4 Improved Initiative); Spd 20 ft.; AC 18 (+1 Dex, +7 *+1 banded*); Atk +9 melee (bastard sword 1d10+5/crit 19–20/x2); AL LN; SV Fort +6, Ref +2, Will +1; Str 16, Dex 13, Con 14, Int 12, Wis 11, Cha 10.

Skills and Feats: Climb +0, Listen +2, Intimidate +7, Spot +3, Innuendo +2, Search +2, Sense Motive +5; Blind-Fight, Combat Reflexes, Dodge, Exotic Weapon Proficiency (bastard sword), Weapon Focus (bastard sword), Weapon Specialization (bastard sword).

Possessions: Masterwork bastard sword, *+1 banded mail,* 2 *potions of cure light wounds,* 10 gp.

McNeil

male human Ftr2: CR 2; Medium-size humanoid (5-ft. 11-in. tall); HD 2d10+2; hp 17 Init +6 (+2 Dex, +4 Improved Initiative); Spd 20 ft.; AC 18 (+2 Dex, +5 chainmail, +2 large shield); Atk +6 melee (1d8+2/crit 19–20/x2, longsword), + 4 ranged (1d6/crit 19–20/x3, light crossbow); AL CE; SV Fort +4, Ref +2, Will –1; Str 15, Dex 14, Con 13, Int 10, Wis 8, Cha 12.

Skills and Feats: Climb +2, Hide +0, Search +1; Cleave, Improved Initiative, Power Attack, Weapon Focus (longsword).

Possessions: Masterwork longsword, light crossbow and 10 bolts, 3 flasks of alchemist's fire, loot from Verlaine's house.

Nikko

male human Clr2/Rog1: CR 3; Medium-size humanoid; HD 2d8 (cleric) + 1d6 (rogue); 15 hp; Init +5 (+1 Dex, +4 Improved Initiative); Spd 30 ft., swim 15 ft.; AC 12 (+1 Dex, +1 *ring of protection*); Atk +3 melee (1d6+1/crit 19–20/x2, short sword); SQ spells; AL CE; SV Fort +3, Ref +3, Will +5; Str 12, Dex 13, Con 11, Int 11, Wis 14, Cha 10.

Skills and Feats: Concentration +6, Disguise +6, Hide +4, Knowledge (arcana) +4, Move Silently +5, Spot +5; Dodge, Combat Casting, Improved Initiative.

Spells Prepared (4/4): 0—detect magic, read magic, resistance (x2); 1st—*bane, magic weapon, obscuring mist, protection from good*.*

*Domain Spell. Domains: Destruction (smite 1/day, +4 attack, +2 damage); Evil (+1 to cast evil spells).

Possessions: Concealed short sword, *potion of alter self, ring of protection (+1),* incriminating documents.

Slaan

male human Rog5/Asn1: HD 6d6; hp 21; Init +3 (Dex); Spd 30 ft.; AC 17 (+3 Dex, +2 chainmail, +1 *amulet of natural armor*); Atk + 7 melee (1d6+2/crit 18–20/x2, *+1 rapier*) or + 5 melee (1d4+1/crit x3, punching dagger), +7 ranged (1d6/crit x3, short bow); SA sneak attack +4d6, death attack (study 3 rounds, sneak attack to paralyze or kill target), spells; AL CE; SV Fort +1, Ref +9, Will +2; Str 12, Dex 16, Con 11, Int 14, Wis 13, Cha 10.

Skills and Feats: Climb +10, Disguise +9, Escape Artist +10, Hide +12, Listen +10, Move Silently +12, Search +9, Spot +6; Dodge, Point Blank Shot, Weapon Finesse (rapier), Ambidexterity.

Spells (1): 1st—spider climb.

Possessions: Amulet of natural armor (+1), +1 rapier, potion of cat's grace, 2 potions of cure light wounds, masterwork shortbow and 10 arrows, masterwork punching dagger, 3 flasks of alchemist's fire, loot from Verlaine's house, false contract.

Weymouth

human War2: CR 1; Medium-size humanoid (6-ft. 1-in. tall); HD 2d8+2; hp 13; Init +6 (+2 Dex, +4 Improved Initiative); Spd 20 ft.; AC 16 (+2 Dex, +4 scale); Atk +4 melee (1d10+2/crit 19–20/x2, bastard sword); SV Fort +4, Ref +2, Will +1; AL N; Str 14, Dex 14, Con 13, Int 11, Wis 12, Cha 10.

Skills and Feats: Climb +2, Intimidate +1, Jump +2, Listen +4; Exotic Weapon Proficiency (bastard sword), Improved Initiative.

Possessions: 10 gp.

Handout A: Milos's Book

Handout B: Drac's Speech

This evening, Councilor Verlaine and the clergy of the God of Knowledge have been slain. Their murderers are the adventurers who of late discovered the caverns beneath our town. After an investigation by the Council and the City Watch, we have pieced together the truth.

Chief Councilor Verlaine, that great servant to the city of Freeport, heard rumors about town of unwholesome activities at the temple to the God of Knowledge. He hired the wandering mercenaries to investigate. They made a tremendous discovery: The temple and its priesthood were a cover for the Brotherhood of the Yellow Sign, a grotesque cult of serpent people. The mercenaries joined the temple to gain its secrets, but they proved treacherous to both masters. They revealed the caves beneath the city and threatened to expose even more secrets unless the Brotherhood paid them a fortune in gold.

The Brotherhood agreed to their demands, on condition that the mercenaries accept one final task for their serpent masters—assassinating their erstwhile employer, Councilor Verlaine. The double-crossers carried out the grim job, but they quickly found themselves double-crossed. The Brotherhood refused to pay them their blood money. The mercenaries went mad with rage and slaughtered the cultists, but were killed themselves in the battle.

We mourn the loss of Councilor Verlaine, but his efforts brought this menace to light—and rooted it out of town, once and for all.

Rollo

Race: *Gnome*
Sex: *Male*
Class: *Fighter*
Level: *3*
Alignment: *Neutral Good*

Strength: *16 (+3)*
Dexterity: *14 (+2)*
Constitution: *17 (+3)*
Intelligence: *14 (+2)*
Wisdom: *12 (+1)*
Charisma: *10 (0)*

Hit Points: *34*
Armor Class: *17 (+1 size, +2 Dex, +4 Scale Mail)*
Speed: *15 ft.*
Initiative: *+2*

Fort Save: *+6*
Ref Save: *+3*
Will Save: *+2*

Melee Attack Bonus: *+7*
Ranged Attack Bonus: *+6*

Weapons: *Gnome Hooked Hammer +7 (1d6+4, x3 and 1d4+4, x4), Short Bow +6 (1d6, x3)*

Feats: *Ambidexterity, Exotic Weapon Proficiency (Gnome Hooked Hammer), Two Weapon Fighting, Weapon Focus (Gnome Hooked Hammer)*

Skills: *Alchemy +5, Climb +8, Hide +7, Jump +5, Listen +5, Ride +4, Spot +3, Swim +6*

Languages: *Common, Draconic, Giant, Gnome*

Height: *3'8"*
Weight: *47 pounds*
Size: *Small*
Age: *56*

Magic Items: *+1 Gnome Hooked Hammer, Cure Light Wounds Potion*

Equipment: *Backpack, bedroll, crowbar, explorer's outfit, flint and steel, quiver with 20 arrows, 3 torches.*

Money: *21 gp*

Malevir

Race: *Half Elf*
Sex: *Male*
Class: *Sorcerer*
Level: *3*
Alignment: *Chaotic Good*

Strength: *9 (-1)*
Dexterity: *17 (+3)*
Constitution: *15 (+2)*
Intelligence: *12 (+1)*
Wisdom: *12 (+1)*
Charisma: *17 (+3)*

Hit Points: *15*
Armor Class: *14 (+1 ring of protection, +3 Dex)*
Speed: *30 ft.*
Initiative: *+3*

Fort Save: *+2*
Ref Save: *+4*
Will Save: *+4*

Melee Attack Bonus: *0*
Ranged Attack Bonus: *+4*

Weapons: *Light Crossbow +4 (1d8, 19-20, x2), Light Mace 0 (1d6-1, x2)*

Feats: *Combat Casting, Dodge*

Skills: *Concentration +6, Knowledge (Arcana) +5, Listen +4, Spellcraft +6, Spot +3*

Languages: *Common, Dwarven, Elven*

Spells: *0-level (6): daze, detect magic, disrupt undead, open/close, resistance; 1st level (6): mage armor, magic missile, sleep*

Height: *5'3"*
Weight: *142 pounds*
Size: *Medium*
Age: *25*

Magic Items: *+1 ring of protection, 2 cure moderate wounds potions*

Equipment: *Backpack, bedroll, ink (vial), inkpen, parchment (sheaf), quiver with 20 bolts, sealing wax, signet ring, traveler's outfit.*

Money: *14 gp*

Alaina

Race: *Human*
Sex: *Female*
Class: *Rogue*
Level: *3*
Alignment: *Neutral Good*

Strength: *14 (+2)*
Dexterity: *18 (+4)*
Constitution: *13 (+1)*
Intelligence: *15 (+2)*
Wisdom: *11 (0)*
Charisma: *13 (+1)*

Hit Points: *18*
Armor Class: *16 (+4 Dex, +2 Leather Armor)*
Speed: *30 ft.*
Initiative: *+4*

Fort Save: *+2*
Ref Save: *+7*
Will Save: *+1*

Melee Attack Bonus: *+4*
Ranged Attack Bonus: *+6*

Weapons: *2 Short Swords +4 (1d6+2, 19-20, x2), Light Crossbow +6 (1d8, 19-20, x2)*

Feats: *Ambidexterity, Two Weapon Fighting, Weapon Finesse (Short Sword)*

Skills: *Appraise +6, Bluff +6, Climb +4, Diplomacy +3, Disable Device +8, Escape Artist +6, Gather Info +6, Hide +10, Listen +5, Move Silently +10, Open Lock +10, Search +6, Spot +5, Tumble +8, Use Rope +5*

Languages: *Common, Elven, Orc*

Height: *5"8"*

Weight: *160 pounds*

Size: *Medium*

Age: *19*

Magic Items: *Bag of Holding (Type 1), Potion of Vision*

Equipment: *Backpack, bedroll, caltrops, explorer's outfit, flint and steel, pouch, quiver with 20 bolts, signal whistle, silk rope (50'), thieves' tools.*

Money: *15 gp*

Thorgrim

Race: *Dwarf*
Sex: *Male*
Class: *Cleric*
Deity: *God of Valor*
Level: *3*
Alignment: *Lawful Good*

Strength: *14 (+2)*
Dexterity: *10 (0)*
Constitution: *17 (+3)*
Intelligence: *12 (+1)*
Wisdom: *15 (+2)*
Charisma: *10 (0)*

Hit Points: *24*
Armor Class: *17 (+4 Scale Mail, +3 Spined Shield)*
Speed: *15 ft.*
Initiative: *+4 (Improved Initiative)*

Fort Save: *+6*
Ref Save: *+1*
Will Save: *+5*

Melee Attack Bonus: *+4*
Ranged Attack Bonus: *+2*

Weapons: *Longsword +5 (1d8+2, 19-20, x2), Dagger +4 (1d4+2, 19-20, x2)*

Feats: *Improved Initiative, Martial Weapon Proficiency (Longsword), Power Attack, Weapon Focus (Longsword)*

Skills: *Concentration +5, Diplomacy +4, Heal +6, Knowledge (Religion) +4, Sense Motive +3, Spellcraft +3*

Languages: *Celestial, Common, Dwarven*

Spells: *4 0-level, 3+1 1st level, 2+1 2nd level*

Domains: *Good, War*

Common Spell Selection: *0-level: cure minor wounds, detect magic, guidance, light; 1st level: command, doom, entropic shield, protection from evil; 2nd level: bull's strength, hold person, spiritual weapon*

Height: *4'4"*

Weight: *144 pounds*

Size: *Medium*

Age: *71*

Magic Item: *Spined Shield*

Equipment: *Backpack, bedroll, explorer's outfit, holy symbol, scroll case, 3 torches, whetstone*

Money: *24 gp*

Appendix 2: Licensing Agreements

Continued on page 32
Continued from page 1
...Open Game Content except as expressly licensed in another, independent Agreement with the owner of such Trademark. The use of any Product Identity in Open Game Content does not constitute a challenge to the ownership of that Product Identity. The owner of any Product Identity used in Open Game Content shall retain all rights, title and interest in and to that Product Identity.
8. Identification: If you distribute Open Game Content You must clearly indicate which portions of the work that you are distributing are Open Game Content.
9. Updating the License: Wizards or its designated Agents may publish updated versions of this License. You may use any authorized version of this License to copy, modify and distribute any Open Game Content originally distributed under any version of this License.
10 Copy of this License: You MUST include a copy of this License with every copy of the Open Game Content You Distribute.
11. Use of Contributor Credits: You may not market or advertise the Open Game Content using the name of any Contributor unless You have written permission from the Contributor to do so.
12 Inability to Comply: If it is impossible for You to comply with any of the terms of this License with respect to some or all of the Open Game Content due to statute, judicial order, or governmental regulation then You may not Use any Open Game Material so affected.
13 Termination: This License will terminate automatically if You fail to comply with all terms herein and fail to cure such breach within 30 days of becoming aware of the breach. All sublicenses shall survive the termination of this License.
14 Reformation: If any provision of this License is held to be unenforceable, such provision shall be reformed only to the extent necessary to make it enforceable.
15 COPYRIGHT NOTICE
Open Game License v 1.0 Copyright 2000, Wizards of the Coast, Inc.

D20 SYSTEM TRADEMARK LICENSE
Version 0.4
1. Definitions.
1.1. "License" means this document.
1.2. "Publication" means any distribution of material under the terms of this License.
1.3. "D20 System Trademarks" means the words "D20 System", and the D20 System logo.
1.4. "D20 System Reference Document" means the copyrighted work owned by Wizards of the Coast identified by that name.
1.5. Each licensee is addressed as "You".
2. The License.
2.1 Offer and Acceptance:
Wizards of the Coast offers You the right to Accept the terms of this License.
You are permitted to use the D20 System Trademarks only in compliance with this License. Use of the Trademarks under any other circumstances is permissible only with explicit written permission from Wizards of the Coast.
Distribution of any Publication which uses the D20 System Trademarks indicates your acceptance of the terms of this License.
2.2 Consideration
In consideration for agreeing to use this License, Wizards of the Coast hereby grants You a world-wide, royalty-free, non-exclusive license to use the D20 System Trademarks as described in this License.
3. Terms and Conditions.
3.1 Limitation of License
3.1.1. No Publication distributed under the terms of this License may contain information on creating characters compatible with the D20 System Reference Document v0.0.
3.1.2. No Publication distributed under the terms of this License may contain information explaining the effects on characters of earning experience or advancing in "level" as that term is defined in the D20 System Reference Document v0.0.
3.1.3. The document known as the D20 System Reference Document v0.0 contains a section titled "Restricted Terms and Definitions". You may not use any term described in that section in any way other than as described in that section in a Publication covered by this License. If the D20 System Reference Document is revised by Wizards of the Coast, you may use any version of the "Restricted Terms and Definitions" section of any version of the D20 System Reference Document issued by Wizards of the Coast.
3.2. Required Notices
3.2.1. You must include a copy of this License with every Publication covered by this License that you distribute.
3.3. Wizards of the Coast Logos and Trademarks.
3.3.1. You may place a notice in the Publication that reads: "Requires the use of the Dungeons & Dragons(R) Player's Handbook, Third Edition, published by Wizards of the Coast(R)." If typography permits, the "(R)" indicia should be converted to the recognized "circle R" character.
3.3.2. If you use the provisions in 3.3.1. you must attach the following notice to the Publication: "Dungeons & Dragons(R) and Wizards of the Coast(R) are Registered Trademarks of Wizards of the Coast, and are used with Permission." If typography permits, the "(R)" indicia should be converted to the recognized "circle R" character.
3.3.3. You may not use the Dungeons & Dragons(R) or Wizards of the Coast(R) trademarks in advertising or in any material separate from the Publication, or in any other way other than that described in Section 3.3.1 and 3.3.2.
3.4. Use of the D20 System Logo
3.4.1. If the Publication is not an electronic file, You must include on the either the front, spine, or back cover of a Publication distributed under the terms of this License the graphical icon known as the "D20 System" logo, which must appear at a size no smaller than .5 (one half) inches by .5 (one half) inches.
3.4.2. If the Publication is an electronic file, the "d20 System" logo must appear in the first area of the Publication displayed when a user views the Publication under normal conditions. The logo must not be smaller than .5 (one half) inches by .5 (one half) inches.
3.4.3. If an Electronic Publication cannot reproduce a graphic element (for example, an ASCII text file), the file must contain the text "This file contains material based on the D20 System. The D20 System and the D20 System logo are trademarks owned by Wizards of the Coast and used under the terms of the D20 Trademark License."
3.4.4. The logo may not be obscured by any other graphic element.
3.4.5. No other alterations of the "D20 System" logo are permissible.
3.5. Permission to use the D20 System Trademarks
3.5.1. You are granted permission to use the "D20 System" Trademarks in advertising connected with a Publication distributed under the terms of this License.
3.5.2. You are granted permission to use the D20 System Trademarks in advertising copy and package copy to describe any Publication distributed under the terms of this License.
3.5.3. You are prohibited from claiming ownership or Trademark interest in the "D20 System" logo, or the "D20 System" trademarks.
3.5.4. You are prohibited from using the "D20 System" logo or the "D20 System" Trademarks in association with a Publication that does not include content derived at least in part from the D20 System Reference Document.
4. Inability to Comply Due to Statute or Regulation.
If it is impossible for You to comply with any of the terms of this License with respect to some or all of the Covered Materials due to statute, judicial order, or governmental regulation then You may not Publish any Covered Material so affected.
6. TERMINATION.
This License and the rights granted hereunder will terminate automatically if You fail to comply with all terms herein and fail to cure such breach within 30 days of becoming aware of the breach. All sublicenses to the Covered Materials which are properly granted shall survive any termination of this License. Provisions which, by their nature, must remain in effect beyond the termination of this License shall survive.
7. MISCELLANEOUS.
If any provision of this License is held to be unenforceable, such provision shall be reformed only to the extent necessary to make it enforceable.